GENERAL TOPOLOGY

GENERAL TOPOLOGY

WOLFGANG FRANZ
Professor of Mathematics
University of Frankfurt-on-Main

Translated from the German by
LEO F. BORON
The Pennsylvania State University

With the assistance of
ROBERT L. BLEFKO
ROBERT C. MOORE
SAMUEL D. SHORE
JAMES L. SIEBER
The Pennsylvania State University

FREDERICK UNGAR PUBLISHING CO.
NEW YORK

Translated from the second German edition of
Topologie: I, Allgemeine Topologie

By arrangement with
Walter de Gruyter & Co., Berlin

Printed in the United States of America

Library of Congress Catalog Card No. 65-28047

TO MY WIFE RUTH

CONTENTS

Part II

SPECIAL CLASSES OF SPACES

Part III

METRIC SPACES

Part IV

RUDIMENTS OF DIMENSION THEORY

INTRODUCTION

The word "topology" is derived from the Greek word τόπος, which means "place," "position" or "space." Accordingly, topology is the science of space; it analyzes the space concept and investigates the properties of general spaces. It is therefore a subdiscipline of geometry. This does not keep it from being in close and fruitful relation to analysis and algebra. It provides analysis with geometric foundations; it receives, on the other hand, essential stimuli from analysis (cf. algebraic functions, algebraic geometry) and, in certain areas, it develops further in common with analysis (cf. functional analysis). From algebra as the fundamentally basic and auxiliary discipline of mathematics it takes essential helping material (e.g., linear algebra, group and module theory) and gives it, in turn, important new results (e.g., homological algebra). However, the proper goal of topology is always the acquisition of geometric knowledge.

In topology the concept of space is considered to be as general as possible; it should comprise everything which in the widest sense of the word deserves the name space. To this concept belong, besides the fundamental basic models (the ordinary 3-dimensional Euclidean space R^3 and the n-dimensional space R^n, with $n = 1, 2, 3, \ldots$ and all subsets of R^n), the infinite-dimensional Hilbert space H, the non-Euclidean spaces and the spaces of Riemannian geometry, as well as more general formations, e.g., the 4-dimensional set of lines in R^3, the set of ellipsoids in R^n, the phase spaces in physics, matrix spaces and function spaces, and many other more general spaces which will not be described here. Naturally, it is not a matter here of the particular properties of one or another of these examples, but rather of the characteristic properties common to all these spaces. Since topology strives for the most penetrating analysis possible of the space concept, it has not only mathematical, but also has philosophical, characteristics (e.g. concerning the theory of cognition), especially in the fundamental portions. Whereas a much discussed classical philosophical teaching (cf. I. Kant, 1724–1804) asserts that the Euclidean geometry of R^3 is the necessary form of human space perception, the beginning chapters of the following presentation show how far the new investigation is removed from this standpoint.

The point of departure and the methods of topology as well as its relations to its neighbor disciplines can be indicated by an especially important example, namely the domain of real numbers, which certainly is of fundamental importance for many other portions of mathematics. Real numbers can be added and multiplied, and the laws which addition and multiplication obey can be derived from fewer basic laws, the so-called field laws. Algebra investigates these basic laws and their consequences. It considers more general systems which are defined axiomatically and in which combining operations similar to addition and multiplication with the same or similar basic rules as the axioms are present. Thus, one arrives at the concepts of field, ring, group, and others, and the theory of these algebraic structures. Topology is not interested, or in any case not directly interested, in the combining operations of the real numbers or their generalizations. It directs its attention more toward those properties which the real numbers have, say, due to the fact that the numerical sequence $1, \frac{1}{2}, \frac{1}{3}, \ldots$ has the limit zero. It deals with the concepts of neighborhood, proximity or the property of being neighboring, openness or closedness of sets of real numbers, continuity of real-valued functions, and similar concepts. From among these concepts, it chooses the simplest possible and the least number possible as primitive concepts. From among the properties of these primitive concepts the simplest possible and the least number possible are chosen as axioms. Thus, one arrives at the fundamental concept of a general topological space, entirely analogous to the above-described procedure in algebra. Compare, say, the later Definitions 2.1 or 4.1. The structure proper of topology consists of the properties of the topological spaces which are derived from these axioms and of such classes of special spaces that can be derived from them by further restrictive axioms.

Moreover, from this viewpoint, the role of analysis, i.e. of the theory of functions of a real variable, appears as follows: It is a composite structure which rests partly on algebraic, partly on topological, axioms, and consequently exhibits a more complicated form than algebra and topology. Stated precisely, a further structure, that of order, also plays a role, which will not be gone into here.

Since in the sequel, an axiomatic construction of topology will be given, knowledge from other domains is basically not required for understanding. Nonetheless it is expected that the reader is to some extent acquainted with the fundamental facts of real analysis, with algebra and with elementary geometry for the following two reasons: First, it contributes to the understanding of and to a correct appreciation of the line of reasoning in an axiomatic structure if one already has an approximate idea of at least the roughest features of what is to be expected and if one can judge the extent and the validity or non-validity of general theorems by comparison with already known special models. Furthermore, from the beginning we must assume as known and use for the examples of a general theory certain basic facts from the areas named above. For those who are less experienced in the reading of mathematical literature, let us furthermore mention the following: The discussion and, in particular, the proofs are generally kept concise; they require a precise thinking through of all details—including those which are not carried out completely. It is best if one completes the deductions independently in detail (with paper and pencil!) and especially if one prepares numerous figures and position sketches, which can be adjoined here only in a few cases due to lack of space.

Part I

THEORY OF GENERAL TOPOLOGICAL SPACES

Chapter 1

AXIOMATIC FOUNDATIONS

§1. Preparation: Metric Spaces

In this section, we shall not yet treat general topological spaces, but rather, as a preliminary step, a somewhat simpler but important special class of spaces—the so-called metric spaces. This introduction serves primarily to prepare examples and to lead to the axioms of topological spaces, to be given later, so that they appear completely plausible to the reader. It is not until Chapter 6 that the theory of metric spaces will be developed in detail for their own sake.

1.1 Definition: A *metric structure*, or, briefly, a *metric*, on a set $\mathfrak{X}$ is given when to each pair x, y of elements of $\mathfrak{X}$ there is assigned a real number $d(x, y) \geqq 0$ satisfying the axioms:

[M 1] $d(x, y) = 0$ if, and only if, $x = y$.
[M 2] $d(y, x) = d(x, y)$.
[M 3] *Triangle axiom*: $d(x, z) \leqq d(x, y) + d(y, z)$.

1.2 Definition: A set $\mathfrak{X}$ together with a metric on $\mathfrak{X}$ is called a *metric space*. We say that the set $\mathfrak{X}$ is *equipped with a metric*. The set $\mathfrak{X}$ is called the *base set* of the metric space. The elements of $\mathfrak{X}$ are called *points* and $d(x, y)$ is called the *distance* between the points x and y.

As the examples to be given later show, there can very well be given different metrics on the same set $\mathfrak{X}$ by means of different distance functions $d(x, y)$ and $d'(x, y)$.

The distance function $d(x, y)$ is subject to two further rules which are similar to the triangle inequality:

$$| d(x, z) - d(z, y) | \leqq d(x, y)$$

(*2nd triangle inequality*)

$$| d(x, y) - d(x', y') | \leqq d(x, x') + d(y, y')$$

(*rectangle inequality*).

Here, the perpendicular lines denote the absolute value of the corresponding real numbers. The second triangle inequality follows from the first: We have $d(x, z) - d(z, y) \leqq d(x, y)$; by interchange of x and y and combination of the resultant two inequalities, the second triangle inequality follows. The rectangle inequality follows from $d(x, y) \leqq d(x, x') + d(x', y') + d(y', y)$; therefore, $d(x, y) - d(x', y') \leqq d(x; x') + d(y, y')$; by interchange of x and x' and of y and y' and combination of the resultant two inequalitites, the rectangle inequality follows.

1.3 Definition: If p is a point of $\mathfrak{X}$ and $\varepsilon < 0$, then the set

$$\mathfrak{U}_\varepsilon(p) = \{x \mid d(x, p) < \varepsilon\}$$

of all points x with $d(x, p) < \varepsilon$ is called the *spherical neighborhood of p with the radius* ε—briefly, the *ε-neighborhood of p*.

The spherical neighborhoods derive their name from the spheres in three-dimensional Euclidean space R^3 as a special case of a metric space. In arbitrary metric spaces, they are naturally not really spheres; they have only a few properties in common with spheres, as is evident from the following examples.

Examples of metric spaces:

(a) *Euclidean space R^n*. Its points are given in the form

$$\mathfrak{x} = (x_1, \ldots, x_n)$$

with arbitrary real numbers $x_1, \ldots, x_n$. The usual definition of distance is

$$d(\mathfrak{x}, \mathfrak{y}) = \sqrt{\sum_{i=1}^{n} (y_i - x_i)^2}.$$

The fact that axioms [M 1] and [M 2] are valid is obvious. To prove [M 3], it must be shown that

$$\sqrt{\sum (z_i - x_i)^2} \leqq \sqrt{\sum (y_i - x_i)^2} + \sqrt{\sum (z_i - y_i)^2}$$

holds for arbitrary real x_i, y_i, z_i (where the summation is over $i = 1, \ldots, n$). We set $y_i - x_i = a_i, z_i - y_i = b_i$. Then we obtain this inequality by tracing the following steps in reverse:

$$\sum(a_i + b_i)^2 \leqq (\sqrt{\sum a_i^2} + \sqrt{\sum b_i^2})^2 = \sum a_i^2 + \sum b_i^2 + 2\sqrt{\sum a_i^2 \sum b_i^2},$$

$$2 \sum a_i b_i \leqq 2\sqrt{\sum a_i^2 \sum b_i^2},$$

$$(\sum a_i b_i)^2 \leqq \sum a_i^2 \cdot \sum b_i^2.$$

This last inequality is the Cauchy-Schwarz inequality, which we can assume to be known to the reader.

In the case $n = 3$, the spherical neighborhoods $\mathfrak{U}_\varepsilon(p)$ are ordinary solid spheres excluding the boundary of the sphere.

(a′) We again start with the same Euclidean space R^n, but now we choose another metric:

$$d'(\mathfrak{x}, \mathfrak{y}) = \mathrm{Max} \mid y_i - x_i \mid, \text{ for } i = 1, \ldots, n.$$

The validity of axioms [M 1] and [M 2] is again clear. We obtain [M 3] as follows:

$$\begin{aligned} d'(\mathfrak{x}, \mathfrak{z}) &= \mathrm{Max} \mid z_i - x_i \mid = \mid z_{i_0} - x_{i_0} \mid \\ &= \mid (y_{i_0} - x_{i_0}) + (z_{i_0} - y_{i_0}) \mid \leqq \mid y_{i_0} - x_{i_0} \mid + \mid z_{i_0} - y_{i_0} \mid \\ &\leqq \mathrm{Max} \mid y_i - x_i \mid + \mathrm{Max} \mid z_i - y_i \mid = d'(x, y) + d'(y, z). \end{aligned}$$

Here, i_0 is any one of the indices $i = 1, \ldots, n$ such that $\mid z_i - x_i \mid$ is a maximum. The spherical neighborhoods $\mathfrak{U}_\varepsilon(p)$ are the cubes with edges parallel to the coordinate axes having length of edge 2ε and p as center.

(a″) We equip Euclidean space R^n with yet another metric:

$$d''(\mathfrak{x}, \mathfrak{y}) = \sum_{i=1}^{n} \mid y_i - x_i \mid.$$

The validity of the axioms is proved similar to the way this was done in (a'). In the case R^3, the spherical neighborhoods are octahedra about p as midpoint and, in the case of R^n, they are the corresponding generalized polytopes.

(b) *Hilbert space H.* H consists of all sequences $\mathfrak{x} = (x_1, x_2, \ldots)$ of real numbers with convergent sum of squares, $\sum x_i^2$, summed over $i = 1, 2, \ldots$. The distance is defined analogous to the way this was done in example (a):

$$d(\mathfrak{x}, \mathfrak{y}) = \sqrt{\sum (y_i - x_i)^2}.$$

But here the convergence of the infinite series under the square root must be proved. In fact, we have that

$$\sum_{i=1}^{N} (y_i - x_i)^2 = \sum_{i=1}^{N} y_i^2 + \sum_{i=1}^{N} x_i^2 - 2 \sum_{i=1}^{N} x_i y_i.$$

As N increases, the first two sums in the right member remain bounded according to our assumption, whereas the last summand in the right member remains bounded according to the Cauchy-Schwarz inequality:

$$\left(\sum_{i=1}^{N} x_i y_i \right)^2 \leqq \sum_{i=1}^{N} x_i^2 \cdot \sum_{i=1}^{N} y_i^2.$$

Therefore, the series is convergent and the distance is well defined. The validity of axioms [M 1] and [M 2] is immediate. [M 3] follows by passing to the limit in the corresponding formula in (a).

An especially important subset of Hilbert space H is the Hilbert cube (or parallelepiped) $\mathscr{P}$, which consists of points $\mathfrak{x} = (x_1, x_2, \ldots)$ with

$$0 \leqq x_n \leqq \frac{1}{2^n} \quad \text{for } n = 1, 2, \ldots$$

Since $\Sigma (1/2^n)^2$ converges, these points $\mathfrak{x}$ certainly belong to H.

(c) Let $\mathfrak{X}$ be the set of continuous real-valued functions $f(x)$ defined on the interval $0 \leqq x \leqq 1$ and let

$$d(f, g) = \sqrt{\int_0^1 (g(x) - f(x))^2 dx}.$$

To prove [M 1] we observe that the integral of a continuous function $h^2(x)$ on $0 \leqq x \leqq 1$ can vanish only when $h(x) = 0$ for all x. [M 3] is obtained from the Cauchy-Schwarz inequality for integrals:

$$\left(\int_0^1 f(x) g(x) dx \right)^2 \leqq \int_0^1 f^2(x) dx \cdot \int_0^1 g^2(x) dx$$

in a way analogous to the way this is done in example (a).

(c′) One can also introduce other metrics in the set of the preceding example, for instance, by the definition:

$$d'(f, g) = \text{Max} \mid g(x) - f(x) \mid \text{for } 0 \leqq x \leqq 1.$$

We note that a continuous real-valued function in the closed interval $0 \leqq x \leqq 1$ actually takes on its maximum at a point of this closed interval. The proof that the axioms are satisfied is easy; [M 1] and [M 2] are immediate. The proof of [M 3] goes through analogous to the way this is done in example (a′):

$$d'(f, h) = \text{Max} \mid h(x) - f(x) \mid = \mid h(x_0) - f(x_0) \mid,$$

where x_0 denotes a point in the interval $0 \leqq x \leqq 1$ at which $\mid h(x) - f(x) \mid$ is maximal. It follows further that

$$\begin{aligned} d'(f, h) &= \mid (g(x_0) - f(x_0)) + (h(x_0) - g(x_0)) \mid \\ &\leqq \mid g(x_0) - f(x_0) \mid + \mid h(x_0) - g(x_0) \mid \\ &\leqq \text{Max} \mid g(x) - f(x) \mid + \text{Max} \mid h(x) - g(x) \mid = d'(f, g) + d'(g, h). \end{aligned}$$

(d) Finally, we give an example which is essentially further removed from geometric intuition. Let $\mathfrak{X}$ be the set of integers and let p be a fixed prime number. Then, by the p-adic value, or, briefly, the p-value, $\mid a \mid_p$, of an integer a ($\neq 0$) from $\mathfrak{X}$ we understand the real number $\mid a \mid_p = 2^{-e}$ if $a = a_0 p^e$ where a_0 is an integer which is relatively prime to p, whereas we set $\mid 0 \mid_p = 0$. Then the following laws for p-adic values hold: (1) $\mid a \mid_p \geqq 0$, $\mid a \mid_p = 0$ if, and only if, $a = 0$; (2) $\mid ab \mid_p = \mid a \mid_p \cdot \mid b \mid_p$; (3) $\mid a + b \mid_p \leqq \mid a \mid_p + \mid b \mid_p$. Only (3) requires a special proof: If $b = b_0 p^f$ with the integer b_0 relatively prime to p, then $\mid b \mid_p = 2^{-f}$, and if, say, $e \leqq f$, then $a + b = cp^e$, with integer c which is still possibly divisible by p. Hence, we have in fact that $\mid a + b \mid_p \leqq 2^{-e} \leqq \mid a \mid_p + \mid b \mid_p$.

$\mathfrak{X}$ becomes a metric space by means of the following metric which is formed analogous to that of example (a′):

$$d(a, b) = \mid b - a \mid_p.$$

Axioms [M 1] and [M 2] are immediate and [M 3] follows from (3):

$$\begin{aligned} d(a, c) &= \mid c - a \mid_p = \mid (b - a) + (c - b) \mid_p \\ &\leqq \mid b - a \mid_p + \mid c - b \mid_p = d(a, b) + d(b, c). \end{aligned}$$

A spherical neighborhood is simply a special case of a general neighborhood of a point which is defined as follows:

1.4 Definition: A subset U of $\mathfrak{X}$ is called a *neighborhood* of the point p if it contains a spherical neighborhood of p.

For example, in R^2 a circular disc including its boundary is a neighborhood of its center. In the older literature, only the so-called open sets were admitted as neighborhoods, whereas we make use of the above somewhat more expedient definition.

The following four significant facts are valid for neighborhoods:

(U 1) *p belongs to every neighborhood U of p.* This is clear according to the definition of a neighborhood.

(U 2) *If U is a neighborhood of p, then every superset $V \supset U$ is also a neighborhood of p.* This likewise follows directly from the definition.

(U 3) *If U_1 and U_2 are neighborhoods of p, then their intersection $U_1 \cap U_2$ is also a neighborhood of p.* Namely, the smaller of the two spherical neighborhoods of p contained in U_1 and in U_2 respectively is contained in $U_1 \cap U_2$, and this shows that $U_1 \cap U_2$ is a neighborhood of p. The corresponding fact holds for finitely many neighborhoods of p: If U_i $(i = 1, \ldots, r)$ are neighborhoods of p, then $\bigcap U_i$ is also a neighborhood of p.

$\mathfrak{X}$ itself is also a neighborhood of p. This assertion can moreover be looked at as the limiting case $r = 0$ in the preceding statement (see *intersection* in the Index); for this reason, we introduce $\mathfrak{X}$ as a neighborhood of p in this item (i.e. under (U 3)).

(U 4) *A neighborhood U of p is also a neighborhood of all points x of a suitable neighborhood V of p.* Namely, if $\mathfrak{U}_\varepsilon(p)$ is any one of the spherical neighborhoods contained in U (according to the definition) and if x is a point in $\mathfrak{U}_\varepsilon(p)$, then there obviously exists a spherical neighborhood $\mathfrak{U}_\eta(x)$ contained in $\mathfrak{U}_\varepsilon(p)$. $\mathfrak{U}_\eta(x)$ is contained in U so that U is a neighborhood of x. Thus, let $V = \mathfrak{U}_\varepsilon(p)$.

We note that by our definition of a neighborhood, a neighborhood U of p is not necessarily a neighborhood of *all* points of U.

At this point, we interrupt our development which we shall, however, continue in subsequent sections on a more general basis. Namely, we will make our further investigations depend only on the properties (U 1) – (U 4). We will therefore take these properties as the axioms for a new, essentially more general theory—that of general topological spaces.

§ 2. Topological Spaces

Metric spaces are still not general enough for many purposes. There are geometric constructions to which one would like to ascribe the character of a space without its being necessary to assign to each pair of elements a real number as distance. Furthermore, the axiom system for metric spaces is not yet completely satisfactory insofar as the real numbers appear in it; the real numbers, in turn, are based on an extended theory which from the logical viewpoint is not entirely simple. We therefore make the following definition.

2.1 Definition: A *topological structure*—in brief, a *topology* $\mathfrak{T}$—for a set $\mathfrak{X}$ is defined by assigning to each element p of $\mathfrak{X}$ a system $\mathfrak{U}(p)$ of subsets of $\mathfrak{X}$, the so-called *neighborhoods U of p*, satisfying the following four axioms:

[U 1] *$p \in U$ for every neighborhood $U \in \mathfrak{U}(p)$.*

[U 2] *If $U \in \mathfrak{U}(p)$ and $V \supset U$, then $V \in \mathfrak{U}(p)$.*

[U 3] *If $U_1, U_2 \in \mathfrak{U}(p)$, then $U_1 \cap U_2 \in \mathfrak{U}(p)$; $\mathfrak{X} \in \mathfrak{U}(p)$.*

[U 4] *For each $U \in \mathfrak{U}(p)$, there exists a $V \in \mathfrak{U}(p)$ such that $U \in \mathfrak{U}(y)$ for all $y \in V$.*

2.2 Definition: A set $\mathfrak{X}$ together with a topology $\mathfrak{T}$ for $\mathfrak{X}$ is called a *topological space*. The set $\mathfrak{X}$ is said to be *equipped* with the topology $\mathfrak{T}$; the set $\mathfrak{X}$ is called the *carrier set* of the topological space. The elements of $\mathfrak{X}$ are called the *points* of the topological space.

Except for slight changes, axioms [U 1]–[U 4] are the *Hausdorff neighborhood axioms* which were taken as the basis for topology by Hausdorff in his classical work on set theory (see the Bibliography: F. Hausdorff [1]).

We note that for every point $p \in \mathfrak{X}$, the system $\mathfrak{U}(p)$ is non-empty because in every case $\mathfrak{X} \in \mathfrak{U}(p)$. By virtue of [$U$ 1], the empty set $\varnothing$

surely belongs to no system $\mathfrak{U}(p)$. The neighborhood V in [U 4] is a subset of U because every point $y \in V$ has U as a neighborhood and is therefore contained in U according to [U 1].

Every metric space becomes a topological space if neighborhoods are defined as was done at the end of § 1; we have proved there that the neighborhoods of the points of a metric space satisfy axioms [U 1]–[U 4]. One says briefly that every metric space is also a topological space—that a metric structure over a set $\mathfrak{X}$ induces a topological structure. The theory of topological spaces which is developed in the sequel therefore yields at the same time theorems about metric spaces; our examples for metric spaces are at the same time examples for topological spaces.

Although every metric structure gives rise to a topological structure, one cannot state that, conversely, every topological structure arises from some metric structure. In this sense, we make the following definition.

2.3 Definition: A given topological structure $\mathfrak{T}$ over $\mathfrak{X}$, i.e. a topological space $\mathfrak{X}$, is said to be *metrizable* if there exists a metric structure over $\mathfrak{X}$ which induces this topological structure $\mathfrak{T}$. Two metric structures over the same set $\mathfrak{X}$ are said to be *topologically equivalent* if they induce the same topological structure.

We shall be concerned with the problem of the metrizability of a topological space in Chapter 8.

As an example of a trivial topology which can be introduced over every set $\mathfrak{X}$, we give the *discrete topology* which assigns as a neighborhood to each point p of $\mathfrak{X}$ every set containing p. One verifies directly that the axioms [U 1]–[U 4] are satisfied. This topology is metrizable, for example by means of the *discrete metric* which is defined by $d(x, y) = 1$ for $x \neq y$ and $d(x,x) = 0$. In fact, with this metric every point is a neighborhood of itself, and hence every set is a neighborhood of all its points.

We give another, less trivial, example of a topological space $\mathfrak{X}$ and, indeed, one which is not metrizable. The proof of the non-metrizability is not difficult; however, we postpone this proof until we take up the basic treatment of such questions in Chapter 8.

Suppose the set $\mathfrak{X}$ consists of all real-valued, not necessarily continuous, functions f over the real line R^1. First, the following sets of functions h of $\mathfrak{X}$ will serve as neighborhoods of a point f in $\mathfrak{X}$:

$$U = U(\varepsilon; x_1, \ldots, x_n) = \{h \mid | h(x_i) - f(x_i) | < \varepsilon \text{ for } i = 1, \ldots, n\}$$

for every $\varepsilon > 0$ and points $x_1, \ldots, x_n$ in R^1. Further, all supersets of such neighborhoods $U(\varepsilon; x_1, \ldots, x_n)$ will be neighborhoods of f. One sees easily that with these assumptions the neighborhood axioms are satisfied. Axioms [U 1] and [U 2] are immediate. The intersection of $U(\varepsilon; x_1, \ldots, x_n)$ and $U(\varepsilon'; x'_1, \ldots, x'_m)$ evidently contains a neighborhood $U(\eta; x_1, \ldots, x_n, x'_1, \ldots, x'_m)$ with an $\eta \leqq \varepsilon, \varepsilon'$, from which we deduce [$U$ 3]. Also (U 4) is not difficult to prove (following the line of reasoning in [U 4] at the end of § 1).

We note in passing the following property of the above space $\mathfrak{X}$: If $f \in \mathfrak{X}$, $g \in \mathfrak{X}$, $f \neq g$, then there exists a neighborhood U of f and a neighborhood V of g with $U \cap V = \varnothing$; namely, if the inequality $f(x_0) \neq g(x_0)$ holds for the real number x_0, then for each ε with the property that $\varepsilon < \frac{1}{2} | f(x_0) - g(x_0) |$ one can obviously take U as a neighborhood $U(\varepsilon; x_0)$ of f and V as a neighborhood $U(\varepsilon; x_0)$ of g. We shall draw upon this space as an example in various ways.

2.4 Definition: Let A be a subset of the topological space $\mathfrak{X}$.

(1) A point $p \in \mathfrak{X}$ is called an *interior point* of A if there exists a neighborhood $U \subset \mathfrak{U}(p)$ which is contained entirely in A. The set of all interior points of A is called the *interior* of A and is denoted by $\underline{A}$.

(2) A point $p \in \mathfrak{X}$ is called an *exterior point* of A if there exists a neighborhood $U \in \mathfrak{U}(p)$ which is contained entirely in the complement $\complement A$. The set of exterior points of A is called the *exterior* of A.

(3) A point $p \in \mathfrak{X}$ is called a *boundary point* of A if there exist points of A and points of $\complement A$ in every neighborhood of p. The set of all boundary points is called the *boundary* of A and is denoted by ϱA.

Exactly one of the three possibilities in Definition 2.4 occurs for each point $p \in \mathfrak{X}$: If (1) occurs, (2) cannot occur. Otherwise, the intersection of the two given neighborhoods would be a neighborhood of p, which would be contained simultaneously in A and in $\complement A$; naturally, (3) cannot occur then. Likewise, the case (2) excludes the possibilities (1) and (3) and, trivially, (3) excludes the cases (1) and

(2). Conversely, for each point $p \in \mathfrak{X}$ one of the three cases must occur: If (1) and (2) do not occur, the occurrence of (3) follows.

The exterior of A coincides with the interior of $\complement A$. The boundary points of A are partitioned into those which belong to A and those which do not belong to A.

2.5 Definition: A point $p \in \mathfrak{X}$ is called a *contact point* of A if there exist points of A in every neighborhood of p. The set of all contact points is called the *closure* of A and is denoted by $\overline{A}$.

The closure $\overline{A}$ is accordingly the union of the sets A and ϱA. As simple consequences of Definitions 2.4 and 2.5, one can easily verify the following important equalities and inclusions:

$$\underline{A} \subset A \subset \overline{A}, \qquad \underline{\varnothing} = \varnothing = \overline{\varnothing}, \qquad \underline{\mathfrak{X}} = \mathfrak{X} = \overline{\mathfrak{X}},$$

$$\complement \underline{A} = \overline{\complement A}, \qquad \complement \overline{A} = \underline{\complement A}, \qquad \varrho(\complement A) = \varrho A,$$

$$\text{and if } A \subset B, \text{ then } \underline{A} \subset \underline{B}, \overline{A} \subset \overline{B}.$$

From the Definitions 2.4 and 2.5 and the disjunction, established above, among the possibilities (1)–(3) in Definition 2.4, there arise the following partitions of $\mathfrak{X}$ with respect to A (into disjoint summands; cf. "partition" in the Index), which, moreover, is clarified in Fig. 1:

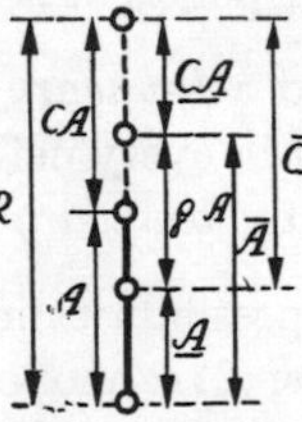

Fig. 1

$$\begin{aligned}\mathfrak{X} &= \underline{A} \cup \varrho A \cup \underline{\mathsf{C}A}\\ &= \underline{A} \cup \overline{\mathsf{C}A} = \overline{A} \cup \underline{\mathsf{C}A};\\ \varrho A &= \overline{A} - \underline{A} = \overline{A} \cap \overline{\mathsf{C}A} = \mathsf{C}(\underline{A} \cup \underline{\mathsf{C}A}).\end{aligned}$$

2.6 Theorem: *$\underline{A}$ can also be thought of as the set of those points which have A as a neighborhood—as a formula, $\underline{A} = \{x \mid A \in \mathfrak{U}(x)\}$.* In other words, *the set A is a neighborhood of all the points of $\underline{A}$ and no others.*

Proof: We take a second formulation: If A is a neighborhood of x, then, according to Definition 2.4, (1), x is an interior point of A.

Conversely, if $x \in \underline{A}$, then there exists a set $U \in \mathfrak{U}(x)$ with $U \subset A$. Then A is also a neighborhood of x according to $[U\ 2]$.

2.7 Definition: A set A is said to be *open* if any one of the following three equivalent conditions is satisfied:

(1) A consists only of interior points of A.
(2) $A = \underline{A}$; it suffices to require that $A \subset \underline{A}$.
(3) $\varrho A \subset \mathsf{C}A$.

A set A is said to be *closed* if any one of the following three equivalent conditions is satisfied:

(1′) The set A contains all its contact points.
(2′) $A = \overline{A}$; it suffices to require that $A \supset \overline{A}$.
(3′) $\varrho A \subset A$.

A set which is closed as well as open is called an *open-closed* set.

The equivalence of these three conditions is clear according to our preceding discussion; this is most simply done using a diagram.

There exist sets A which are neither open nor closed—for example, a circular disc in the Euclidean plane which includes part, but not all, of its circumference. A set A can very well be open and closed—therefore, be open-closed. One must not be disturbed on linguistic grounds here: the concepts "open" and "closed" are not to be conceived of as being contradictory. For example, the sets $\emptyset$ and $\mathfrak{X}$ are open-closed, which fact can be verified by simply applying the definition.

The open-closed subsets of $\mathfrak{X}$ form the point of departure of the theory of connectivity of topological spaces (see § 7).

2.8 Theorem: *A set A is open if, and only if, $\complement A$ is closed; a set A is closed if, and only if, $\complement A$ is open.*

The second part of the theorem obviously asserts the same thing as the first. The proof is yielded most simply from the conditions (3) and (3′) of Definition 2.7 and from $\varrho A = \varrho(\complement A)$.

2.9 Theorem: *A set A is open if, and only if, it is a neighborhood of each of its points.*

This is an immediate consequence of Theorem 2.6 upon applying Definition 2.7 (2) which we introduced in the meantime.

§ 3. Duality Principle

In Definition 2.7 and in Theorem 2.8, there arises a duality between certain concepts and theorems about topological spaces which we shall now consider more precisely. We do this less for abbreviating the proofs, which is inessential, than to obtain a better organization of the facts to be proved.

Let $\mathfrak{X}$ be a topological space which contains all the sets appearing in the sequel as subsets. Let the set A be composed from the sets X, $Y, \ldots$ by means of the operations $\cup$, $\cap$ and the formation of interiors and closures and from the special subsets $\emptyset$ and $\mathfrak{X}$. This we shall express by $A = F(X, Y, \ldots)$ in analogy with the notation for functions and their independent variables. We obtain $\complement A$ by applying the following rules, already proved, on the function F:

$$\complement(X \cup Y) = \complement X \cap \complement Y, \complement \underline{X} = \overline{\complement X}, \complement \emptyset = \mathfrak{X},$$

$$\complement(X \cap Y) = \complement X \cup \complement Y, \complement \overline{X} = \underline{\complement X}, \complement \mathfrak{X} = \emptyset$$

until we arrive at the form $\complement A = F^*(\complement X, \complement Y, \ldots)$. Here, F^* means the function which arises from F upon replacing $\cup$ by $\cap$, the formation of the interior by the formation of the closure and $\emptyset$ by $\mathfrak{X}$, and conversely. Also, henceforth, the asterisk on a function F denotes this "dual" function. Let $B = G(X, Y, \ldots)$ be another set composed from $X, Y, \ldots$. If $A = B$ or $A \subset B$ is a relation between A and B, then it follows that $\complement A = \complement B$ or $\complement A \supset \complement B$, respectively, and for the corresponding functions, say, in the last case, we have

$$(*) \qquad F^*(\complement X, \complement Y, \ldots) \supset G^*(\complement X, \complement Y, \ldots).$$

If the relation $F(X, Y, \ldots) \subset G(X, Y, \ldots)$ holds for arbitrary composite sets $X, Y, \ldots$, then the relation (*) also holds for arbitrary $X, Y, \ldots$. Now if X ranges over all subsets of $\mathfrak{X}$, then so does $\complement X$; likewise, if Y ranges over all subsets of $\mathfrak{X}$, then $\complement Y$ does also, and so on. Therefore, one can simply replace $\complement X, \complement Y, \ldots$ in the relation (*) again by $X, Y, \ldots$. One thus obtains a pair of mutually dual relations

$$\begin{cases} F(X, Y, \ldots) \subset G(X, Y, \ldots), \\ F^*(X, Y, \ldots) \supset G^*(X, Y, \ldots), \end{cases}$$

which arise from one another by a purely mechanical replacement of $\cup$ by $\cap$, interior by closure, $\emptyset$ by $\mathfrak{X}$, $\subset$ by $\supset$, and by the reverse replacements. One calls this formation process the *duality principle* for topological spaces.

One can add the following supplementary remarks. If some of the composing sets $X, Y, \ldots$ are not arbitrary, but rather are bound by the assumption of being open, then we obviously obtain a correct relation when we make in the dual relation the assumption that the corresponding sets are closed. If instead of a relation between two sets, we are dealing with the assertion that the set $A = F(X, Y, \ldots)$ is open, then the dual assertion that $F^*(X, Y, \ldots)$ is closed holds. In these considerations, one can naturally interchange the words "open" and "closed."

An acceptable foundation of the duality principle really requires a clarification of the basic logical concepts, especially of the concept of "proposition." But we content ourselves with the preceding sketch which in any case suffices for the purposes of the following sections.

The theorems are dually juxtaposed by pairs and we always prove only one of them. The reader can easily derive the other according to the above line of reasoning. We pay attention especially to the fact that in this process the theorems themselves, but not their proofs, are dualized.

3.1 Theorem: *Let λ range over an arbitrary index set Λ and i over the natural numbers* 1, . . ., *n*.

(O 1) The union $\bigcup A_\lambda$ of an arbitrary number of open sets A_λ is open. $\emptyset$ is open.

(A 1) The intersection $\bigcap A_\lambda$ of an arbitrary number of closed sets A_λ is closed. $\mathfrak{X}$ is closed.

(O 2) The intersection $\bigcap A_i$ of a finite number of open sets A_i is open. $\mathfrak{X}$ is open.

(A 2) The union $\bigcup A_i$ of a finite number of closed sets A_i is closed. $\emptyset$ is closed.

Proof: (*O* 1): Let $p \in \bigcup A_\lambda$. Then $p \in A_\lambda$ for at least one λ, and there exists a neighborhood of p which belongs entirely to A_λ. This neighborhood belongs also to $\bigcup A_\lambda$, and this proves that $\bigcup A_\lambda$ is open.

(*O* 2): Let $p \in \bigcap A_i$. Then $p \in A_i$ for every i and there exist neighborhoods $U_i \in \mathfrak{U}(p)$ which are contained entirely in A_i. Then $\bigcap U_i$ is likewise a neighborhood of p according to [*U* 3] and indeed it is a neighborhood contained in $\bigcap A_i$. Therefore, $\bigcap A_i$ is open.

It was already established in connection with Definition 2.7 that $\emptyset$ and $\mathfrak{X}$ are open and closed. Concerning $\emptyset$ as a union set and $\mathfrak{X}$ as an intersection, see the Index under *union* and *intersection*.

The reader should verify by counterexamples that (*O* 2) and (*A* 2) do not hold in general for infinitely many A_i. For instance, in R^1 one obtains a counterexample to (*A* 2) by taking for the A_i the one-point sets $\{p\}$ for all p of a non-closed set.

3.2 Theorem:

The interior $\underline{A}$ is open. *The closure $\overline{A}$ is closed.*

The proof, which is by no means trivial, makes use of [*U* 4] for the first time: Let $x \in \underline{A}$. Then there exists a $U \in \mathfrak{U}(x)$ with $x \in U \subset A$. According to [U 4], there exists a $V \in \mathfrak{U}(x)$ such that $U \in \mathfrak{U}(y)$ for all $y \in V$. Therefore, all y are interior points of A, $V \subset \underline{A}$. This shows that x is an interior point of $\underline{A}$, which is what we were required to prove.

3.3 Theorem:

$\underline{A}$ is the union of all open subsets of A; we say that $\underline{A}$ is the largest open subset of A.

$\overline{A}$ is the intersection of all closed supersets of A; we say that $\overline{A}$ is the smallest closed superset of A.

Proof: Since $\underline{A}$ is open, $\underline{A}$ is taken into account in the formation of the union V of all open subsets of A; therefore, $\underline{A} \subset V$. V is a subset of A and, by virtue of Theorem 3.1, (O 1), V is open. Every point $x \in V$ therefore has a neighborhood which is contained in A and hence every point of V belongs to $\underline{A}$. This means that $V \subset \underline{A}$. The assertion follows by combining these two results.

3.4 Theorem: *A set U is a neighborhood of a point p if, and only if, there exists an open set O such that $x \in O \subset U$.*

Proof: If there exists an open set O such that $p \in O \subset U$, then $O \in \mathfrak{U}(p)$ by virtue of Theorem 2.9, and hence also $U \in \mathfrak{U}(p)$ according to [U 2]. Conversely, if $U \in \mathfrak{U}(p)$, then $p \in \underline{U}$ by virtue of Theorem 2.6, $\underline{U} = O$ is open by virtue of Theorem 3.2, and therefore $p \in \underline{U} = O \subset U$.

3.5 Theorem: *Let A_λ range over a system of arbitrarily many sets with the indices λ. Then the following relations hold:*

a) $\underline{\bigcup A_\lambda} \supset \bigcup \underline{A_\lambda}$, c) $\overline{\bigcap A_\lambda} \subset \bigcap \overline{A_\lambda}$,

b) $\underline{\bigcap A_\lambda} \subset \bigcap \underline{A_\lambda}$, d) $\overline{\bigcup A_\lambda} \supset \bigcup \overline{A_\lambda}$.

Proof: a): Let $x \in \bigcup \underline{A_\lambda}$, say, $x \in \underline{A_0}$. Then x is an interior point of A_0 and it is thus also an interior point of $\bigcup A_\lambda$, i.e. $x \in \underline{\bigcup A_\lambda}$.

b): If x belongs to $\underline{\bigcap A_\lambda}$, then there exists a neigborhood of x which belongs entirely to $\bigcap A_\lambda$, i.e. it belongs to every A_λ. Then x is an interior point of each set A_λ, $x \in \underline{A}_\lambda$, and this means that x belongs to $\bigcap \underline{A}_\lambda$.

Relations c) and d) are proved similarly.

In general, the equality sign does not hold in any of the inclusions of the theorem. In the case a), consider in the reals R^1 the sets $A_1 = \{x \mid -1 \leqq x \leqq 0\}$ and $A_2 = \{x \mid 0 \leqq x \leqq +1\}$; we have that $\underline{A_1 \cup A_2} \neq \underline{A}_1 \cup \underline{A}_2$. For the inclusions b) and d), we can easily find examples of the sort given in connection with Theorem 3.1. It is particularly remarkable that in this case one uses an infinite number of sets A_λ; namely, the following theorem holds.

3.6 Theorem: $\underline{A \cap B} = \underline{A} \cap \underline{B}, \overline{A \cup B} = \overline{A} \cup \overline{B}$.

Proof: We have already proved in the last theorem that $\underline{A \cap B} \subset \underline{A} \cap \underline{B}$. $\underline{A \cap B}$ is the maximal open set contained in $A \cap B$; $\underline{A} \cap \underline{B}$ is an open set contained in $A \cap B$. Thus, $\underline{A \cap B} \supset \underline{A} \cap \underline{B}$. Combination of these results yields the first equality of the theorem.

3.7 Theorem:

If O is open and A closed, then $O - A$ is open.

If A is closed and O open, then $A - O$ is closed.

Proof: We have that $O - A = O \cap (\complement A)$. O and $\complement A$ are open; therefore, the intersection is also open.

3.8 Theorem:

If A is open, B arbitrary and $A \cap B = \varnothing$, then also $A \cap \overline{B} = \varnothing$.

If A is closed, B arbitrary and $A \cup B = \mathfrak{X}$, then also $A \cup \underline{B} = \mathfrak{X}$.

Proof: $A \cap B = \varnothing$ means that $B \subset \complement A$. It follows that $\overline{B} \subset \overline{\complement A} = \complement \underline{A} = \complement A$ and this means that $A \cap \overline{B} = \varnothing$.

We now generalize the concept of neighborhood by introducing neighborhoods of arbitrary subsets A of $\mathfrak{X}$ in supplement to Theorem 3.4.

3.9 Definition: A set U is called a *neighborhood* of the set A if there exists an open set O such that $A \subset O \subset U$.

Then, in analogy with the neighborhood axioms [U 1]–[U 3], it is true that a neighborhood U of A always contains A, that together with U also every set $V \supset U$ is a neighborhood of A and, finally, that together with U_1 and U_2 also $U_1 \cap U_2$ is a neighborhood of A. We will not need an analogue to [U 4].

3.10 Theorem: *U is a neighborhood of A if, and only if, U is a neighborhood of all points x in A.*

Proof: If U is a neighborhood of A, then Theorem 3.4 shows that $U \in \mathfrak{U}(x)$ for every $x \in A$. Conversely, let $U \in \mathfrak{U}(x)$ for every $x \in A$. By virtue of Theorem 3.4, then for each $x \in A$ there exists an open set O_x such that $x \in O_x \subset U$. We form $V = \bigcup O_x$ taken over all $x \in A$. V is open according to Theorem 3.1 and is contained in U; V contains A by its construction. Therefore, U is by definition a neighborhood of A.

In analysis one frequently makes use of the concept of accumulation point instead of that of contact point.

3.11 Definition: The point p is called an *accumulation point* of the set A if p is a contact point of $A - \{p\}$. The point $p \in A$ is called an *isolated point* of A if there exists a neighborhood of p in which the only point of A is p. An accumulation point is also called a *limit point.*

Here, $\{p\}$ denotes the set consisting of the single point p. Concerning the terminology *accumulation point*, see Theorem 13.10, at the end of § 13.

3.12 Thereom: *A contact point of A is either an accumulation point of A or it is an isolated point of A; $\overline{A}$ arises from A by adjoining the accumulation points of A.*

Proof: Let p be a contact point of A. If there exists a neighborhood of p which contains no points of A except p, then p is an isolated point of A. Otherwise, there exist in every neighborhood of p further points of $A - \{p\}$, i.e. p is an accumulation point of A. Conversely, every accumulation point of A and every isolated point of A is also a contact point of A.

As an application, let us determine the open subsets of the real line R^1 in the usual topology. To them belong surely the *open intervals* of R^1; these are the sets $(a, b) = \{x \mid a < x < b\}$, $(a, +\infty) = \{x \mid a < x\}$, $(-\infty, b) = \{x \mid x < b\}$ and $(-\infty, +\infty) = R^1$. Furthermore, arbitrary unions of open intervals are open. We now prove the following theorem.

3.13 Theorem: *A non-empty open set O of the real line R^1 is representable as the union of a denumerable number of disjoint open intervals whose endpoints belong to the complementary set $\complement O$.*

The closed subsets of R^1, which are the complements of open sets, are at the same time characterized by this theorem.

Proof: (1) Let $x \in O$. Since O is open, there exists an open interval containing x and contained in O, namely a suitable neighborhood $\mathfrak{U}_\varepsilon(x)$. Let I_x be the union of all the open intervals of this sort. According to [O 1], I_x is open. We shall show that I_x itself is an open interval of this sort—more specifically, that $I_x = (a, b)$, where $a = \inf I_x$ and $b = \sup I_x$; here, $a = -\infty$ or $b = +\infty$ are also admitted. (Concerning *inf* and *sup*, see the Index.) Namely, if $y \in (a, b)$ and, say, $a < y < x$, then there exists according to the definition of a an $x' \in I_x$ with $a < x' < y$, and x' lies together with x in an open interval contained in O. Therefore, y also lies in this interval and hence $y \in I_x$. The same is true when $x < y < b$, and for $y = x$ we likewise have that $y \in I_x$. We therefore have the result that for each $x \in O$ there exists a uniquely determined open interval I_x which contains x and is contained in O and which is contained in no larger open interval of this sort.

(2) If x_1, x_2 are points from O and the corresponding intervals I_{x_1}, I_{x_2} have common points, then $I_{x_1} \cup I_{x_2}$ is an open interval containing x_1 and contained in O. Therefore $I_{x_1} \cap I_{x_2} = I_{x_1}$. Analogously, $I_{x_1} \cap I_{x_2} = I_{x_2}$, so that $I_{x_1} = I_{x_2}$. The distinct intervals I_x are therefore disjoint.

(3) An endpoint a of an interval I_x cannot belong to O for otherwise I_x and I_a would have common points and yet not be coincident, in contradiction to (2).

To complete the proof of the theorem it remains to show that at most a denumerable number of distinct intervals I_x are involved. The following somewhat more general theorem shows this.

3.14 Theorem: *Every system of disjoint open sets in R^n is finite or denumerable.*

Proof: We select in each of the open sets a rational point, i.e., a point all of whose coordinates are rational. This sets up a one-to-one correspondence between the system of open sets and a subset of the rational numbers. Since the set of rational points in R^n is denumerable, the assertion of the theorem follows immediately.

§ 4. U-, O- and K-Topologies

In the preceding discussion, we introduced a topology for a set $\mathfrak{X}$ which was based on the concept of neighborhood—more specifically, on a neighborhood system $\mathfrak{U}(p)$ given for each point $p \in \mathfrak{X}$ as a primitive concept. We shall now become acquainted with another type of topology for the same set $\mathfrak{X}$ which is based on the concept "open" as a primitive concept. In this connection, the concepts "neighborhood," "open," "interior," and so forth, appear in both topologies and refer in both cases to subsets of the same set $\mathfrak{X}$. In order to avoid confusion, we denote—only for the purposes of this section —the topology developed up to this point, based on the neighborhood concept, as the neighborhood topology $\mathfrak{T}_U$, or briefly, as the U-topology. We provide all concepts and notation with the distinguishing U, and, therefore, speak of U-neighborhoods, the system $\mathfrak{U}_U(p)$, U-open sets, the U-interior, and so forth. In contrast to this, we now define, completely independently of the preceding discussion, a new O-topology as follows:

4.1 Definition: An *O-topology* $\mathfrak{T}_O$ for a set $\mathfrak{X}$ is defined if a system $\mathfrak{O}_O$ of subsets of $\mathfrak{X}$, the O-sets, is distinguished in such a way that the following axioms hold:

[O 1] The union of O-sets is again an O-set. $\emptyset$ is an O-set.

[O 2] The intersection of a finite number of O-sets is again an O-set. $\mathfrak{X}$ is an O-set.

The O-sets are also called *O-open.*

We recognize that the axioms [O 1], [O 2] are formed analogously to the assertions (O 1) and (O 2) of Theorem 3.1.

4.2 Definition: A set U is called an *O-neighborhood* of a point p if there exists an O-set O such that $p \in O \subset U$.

The following theorems are valid for O-neighborhoods which are analogous to the previous axioms [U 1], . . ., [U 4], but here they are not axioms, but rather theorems about the topology $\mathfrak{T}_O$, which require a proof.

(U 1) *p is an element of every O-neighborhood U of p.*

(U 2) *Together with U, every set $V \supset U$ is also an O-neighborhood of p.*

(U 3) *The intersection of a finite number of O-neighborhoods of p is again an O-neighborhood of p. $\mathfrak{X}$ is an O-neighborhood of p.*

(U 4) *If U is an O-neighborhood of p, then there exists an O-neighborhood V of p such that U is an O-neighborhood of all points y of V.*

(U 1) and (U 2) are clear according to the definition of O-neighborhoods. (U 3) is verified directly by using [O 2]. Finally, one proves (U 4) by taking for the required O-neighborhood V precisely the O-open set O of Definition 4.2, which is itself certainly a neighborhood of p. The Theorems (U 1)–(U 4) are thus proved.

4.3 Theorem: *A set is O-open if, and only if, it is an O-neighborhood of all its points.*

Proof: If the set A is O-open, then, by Definition 4.2, A is an O-neighborhood for each point $x \in A$. Conversely, if A is an O-neighborhood of all the points $x \in A$, then there exists for each $x \in A$ an O-open set O_x such that $x \in O_x \subset A$. Then $A = \bigcup O_x$ and by [O 1] it is O-open.

The topology $\mathfrak{T}_U$ over $\mathfrak{X}$ constructed in §§ 2, 3 and the topology $\mathfrak{T}_O$ of $\mathfrak{X}$ developed in this section have been considered completely independently. We now show their relationship. First, the statements (O 1) and (O 2) of Theorem 3.1 show that the U-open sets of $\mathfrak{T}_U$ satisfy the axioms [O 1] and [O 2] of $\mathfrak{T}_O$. Therefore, to make correspond to a topology $\mathfrak{T}_U$ a topology $\mathfrak{T}_O$, one need only choose the totality of the U-open sets of $\mathfrak{T}_U$ as the defining system $\mathfrak{O}_O$ of an O-topology. Then the question arises in what relation do the U-neighborhoods of $\mathfrak{T}_U$ stand to the O-neighborhoods of $\mathfrak{T}_O$. Comparison of Theorem 3.4 with Definition 4.2 shows that these two concepts of neighborhood likewise coincide. We summarize the result as follows.

4.4 Theorem: *For every U-topology $\mathfrak{T}_U$ for a set $\mathfrak{X}$ with the defining U-neighborhood systems $\mathfrak{U}_U(p)$, there exists exactly one O-topology $\mathfrak{T}_O$ for $\mathfrak{X}$ whose defining system $\mathfrak{O}_O$ of O-open sets coincides with the totality of the U-open sets of $\mathfrak{T}_U$; the totality of the O-neighborhoods in $\mathfrak{T}_O$ of a point $p \in \mathfrak{X}$ coincides then with $\mathfrak{A}_U(p)$.*

Since the topology $\mathfrak{T}_U$ depends only on the U-neighborhood systems $\mathfrak{U}_U(p)$ and the topology $\mathfrak{T}_O$ only on the system $\mathfrak{O}_O$ of O-open sets, one can, on the basis of this theorem, identify the two topologies, namely $\mathfrak{T}_U$ and the topology $\mathfrak{T}_O$ deduced from it, coextensively with each other. All theorems of both topologies are similar in expression, i.e. they differ only by the distinguishing letters U and O. It is only the starting point which is different, sometimes the neighborhood system and sometimes the open sets are assumed to be the primitive concept. We point out further the decisive role of Theorem 3.4 in these considerations. It characterizes the primitive concept of neighborhood of $\mathfrak{T}_U$ in terms of the concept of U-openness defined in $\mathfrak{T}_U$.

The question yet remains open whether one can obtain all possible topologies $\mathfrak{T}_O$ for $\mathfrak{X}$ by assigning to each topology $\mathfrak{T}_U$ for $\mathfrak{X}$ a topology $\mathfrak{T}_O$ for $\mathfrak{X}$. The following analogue to Theorem 4.4. shows that this is really so.

4.5 Theorem: *For each O-topology $\mathfrak{T}_O$ for a set $\mathfrak{X}$ with the defining system $\mathfrak{O}_O$ of the O-open sets there exists exactly one U-topology $\mathfrak{T}_U$ for $\mathfrak{X}$ whose defining neighborhood system $\mathfrak{A}_U(p)$ for the points $p \in \mathfrak{X}$ coincides with the O-neighborhood systems of the point p in $\mathfrak{T}_O$; the totality of the U-open sets of $\mathfrak{T}_U$ then coincide with the system $\mathfrak{O}_O$.*

The proof proceeds entirely analogously to that of Theorem 4.4. The characterizing theorem concerning $\mathfrak{T}_O$ to be used in this case is Theorem 4.3; it is comparable with Theorem 2.9 concerning the topology $\mathfrak{T}_U$.

Hereby the totality of U- and O-topologies for $\mathfrak{X}$ correspond to one another in one-to-one fashion. It is immaterial for the further construction of the theory which of the two axiomatic approaches, $\mathfrak{T}_U$ or $\mathfrak{T}_O$, one chooses. The reason that we started in Sections 2, 3 from $\mathfrak{T}_U$ is that in the beginning geometric intuition is perhaps more important. It will be evident in the following that $\mathfrak{T}_O$ is in many ways somewhat simpler to handle.

We will characterize axiomatically the topological spaces, in addition to O- and U-topologies, in a third way. In this connection, we take as basic the primitive concept of the interior $\underline{A}$ of a set A.

4.6 Definition: A K*-topology* $\mathfrak{T}_K$ over a set $\mathfrak{X}$ is defined if to every subset A of $\mathfrak{X}$ there is assigned a subset $\underline{A}$ of $\mathfrak{X}$ so that the following axioms are satisfied:

$$[K\ 1]\ \underline{\mathfrak{X}} = \mathfrak{X};\quad [K\ 3]\ \underline{\underline{A}} = \underline{A};$$
$$[K\ 2]\ \underline{A} \subset A;\quad [K\ 4]\ \underline{A \cap B} = \underline{A} \cap \underline{B}.$$

$\underline{A}$ is called the K*-interior* of A.

4.7 Definition: A set A is called K*-open* if $A = \underline{A}$.

For example, $\mathfrak{X}$ is K-open by virtue of [K 1] and $\emptyset$ is K-open inasmuch as, by virtue of [K 2], $\underline{\emptyset} \subset \emptyset$ holds.

4.8 Theorem: *If* $A \subset B$, *then* $\underline{A} \subset \underline{B}$.

Proof: $A \subset B$ is equivalent to $A = A \cap B$. By [K 4], it follows that $\underline{A} = \underline{A \cap B} = \underline{A} \cap \underline{B}$, and this means that $\underline{A} \subset \underline{B}$.

4.9 Theorem: (O 1) *The union* $V = \bigcup A_\lambda$ *of an arbitrary number of* K*-open sets* A_λ *is* K*-open.* (O 2) *If* A_1 *and* A_2 *are* K*-open, then* $A_1 \cap A_2$ *is also* K*-open.*

Proof: (O 1): We have that $\underline{A}_\lambda = A_\lambda$. It follows from $A_\lambda \subset V$ that $\underline{A}_\lambda \subset \underline{V}$ or that $A_\lambda \subset \underline{V}$. It follows further that $V = \bigcup A_\lambda \subset \underline{V}$ and from this that $V = \underline{V}$.

(O 2): It follows from $\underline{A}_1 = A_1$, $\underline{A}_2 = A_2$, by [K 4], that $\underline{A_1 \cap A_2} = \underline{A}_1 \cap \underline{A}_2 = A_1 \cap A_2$.

4.10 Theorem: $\underline{A}$ *is the union of all the* K*-open subsets of* A, *i.e.* $\underline{A}$ *is the largest* K*-open subset of* A.

Proof: $\underline{A}$ is K-open according to [K 3] and a subset of A by virtue of [K 2]. Now, let G be the union of all K-open subsets of A. G is K-open according to Theorem 4.9. Therefore, $\underline{A} \subset G \subset A$. According to Theorem 4.8, it follows that $\underline{\underline{A}} \subset G \subset \underline{A}$, i.e. $\underline{A} \subset G \subset \underline{A}$, and therefore $G = \underline{A}$.

It is now easy, following the pattern of Theorem 4.4 and Theorem 4.5, to let correspond to each O-topology $\mathfrak{T}_O$ for $\mathfrak{X}$ a K-topology $\mathfrak{T}_K$ for $\mathfrak{X}$, and conversely. The open interiors in $\mathfrak{T}_O$ obviously satisfy the axioms [K 1]–[K 4] and motivate the introduction of a corresponding K-topology $\mathfrak{T}_K$. Comparison of Definition 4.7 for $\mathfrak{T}_K$ and Definition 2.7, (2) for $\mathfrak{T}_O$ (or for $\mathfrak{T}_U$, which amounts to the same thing according to the preceding discussion) shows that the open sets in both topologies coincide. In the reversed correspondence, one has to show that the interiors of the two topologies coincide; this is attained by comparison of the Theorems 4.10 for $\mathfrak{T}_K$ and 3.3. for $\mathfrak{T}_O$ and $\mathfrak{T}_U$ respectively. One thus recognizes the equivalence of the U-, O- and K-topologies for $\mathfrak{X}$.

Naturally, one can introduce together with $\mathfrak{T}_O$ in a dual manner a closure topology $\mathfrak{T}_A$ and likewise, together with $\mathfrak{T}_K$, a closure topology $\mathfrak{T}_H$. All these topologies are equivalent. In the sequel, we omit the indices U, O, and so on and we shall prefer one or the other topology on grounds of expediency.

Chapter 2

DEVELOPMENT OF THE THEORY

§ 5. Mappings and Functions

We shall first study briefly the mappings f of a set $\mathfrak{X}$ into a set $\mathfrak{Y}$—in symbols, $f\colon \mathfrak{X} \rightarrow \mathfrak{Y}$. A mapping f assigns to each element $x \in \mathfrak{X}$ a well-defined element $y \in \mathfrak{Y}$. $\mathfrak{X}$ is called the *domain of definition* (or simply the *domain*) of f and $\mathfrak{Y}$ is called the *range of variation* (or simply the *range*) of f. We shall also write $y = f(x)$; y is called the *image* of x, x is called a *pre-image* of y. We also say that f is a *function* which assigns to each x of the domain $\mathfrak{X}$ a y of the range $\mathfrak{Y}$. Each $x \in \mathfrak{X}$ has precisely one image, but one $y \in \mathfrak{Y}$ can have several pre-images. If $A \subset \mathfrak{X}$, then $f(A) = B$ denotes the set of images of the elements of A. It may happen that $f(\mathfrak{X})$ is a proper subset of $\mathfrak{Y}$.

If f has the property that $f(\mathfrak{X}) = \mathfrak{Y}$ and hence that each element of $\mathfrak{Y}$ is an image, then f is said to be *epimorphic* or a *mapping onto* $\mathfrak{Y}$. If f has the property that each element y has at most one pre-image and, hence, that $f(x_1) = f(x_2)$ implies $x_1 = x_2$, then f is said to be a *monomorphic*, or *reversibly single-valued*, or a *one-to-one*, *mapping* of $\mathfrak{X}$ into $\mathfrak{Y}$. If f is epimorphic as well as monomorphic, then f is called an *isomorphic*, or a *one-to-one*, *mapping* of $\mathfrak{X}$ *onto* $\mathfrak{Y}$; f yields a reversibly single-valued relation, a pairing, between the elements of $\mathfrak{X}$ and $\mathfrak{Y}$. In this case, and only in this case, there exists an inverse mapping $f^{-1}\colon \mathfrak{Y} \rightarrow \mathfrak{X}$, which maps $\mathfrak{Y}$ in a reversible single-valued manner onto $\mathfrak{X}$. The equations $y = f(x)$, $x = f^{-1}(y)$ are equivalent to one another. f^{-1} is called the *inverse* of f.

One attributes a meaning to the symbol f^{-1} also for arbitrary mappings $f\colon \mathfrak{X} \rightarrow \mathfrak{Y}$, not only for isomorphic mappings and speaks in an extended sense of an inverse f^{-1} to f. If B is a subset of $\mathfrak{Y}$, then $f^{-1}(B)$ is defined as the set of all pre-images of all the elements of B. $f^{-1}(y)$ is accordingly the set of all pre-images of the element $y \in B$; $f^{-1}(y)$ can be empty or consist of several elements. f^{-1} is therefore generally not a mapping of $\mathfrak{Y}$ into $\mathfrak{X}$, but rather f^{-1} assigns to each subset of $\mathfrak{Y}$ a, perhaps empty, subset of $\mathfrak{X}$. One recognizes immediately the validity of the following two inclusions for arbitrary subsets $A \subset \mathfrak{X}$ and arbitrary subsets $B \subset \mathfrak{Y}$:

$$f^{-1}(f(A)) \supset A, f(f^{-1}(B)) \subset B.$$

In the first relation, the equality sign holds for all $A \subset \mathfrak{X}$ if, and only if, f is monomorphic. In the second relation, the equality sign holds for all $B \subset \mathfrak{Y}$ if, and only if, f is epimorphic. If $\mathfrak{Y} = \bigcup B_\lambda$ is a partition of $\mathfrak{Y}$ into sets B_λ, then $\mathfrak{X} = \bigcup f^{-1}(B_\lambda)$ is a partition of $\mathfrak{X}$.

For the behavior of a mapping with respect to the formation of unions and intersections, the following laws are valid:

$$f(A_1 \cup A_2) = f(A_1) \cup f(A_2),$$
$$f^{-1}(B_1 \cup B_2) = f^{-1}(B_1) \cup f^{-1}(B_2),$$
$$(*) \qquad f(A_1 \cap A_2) \subset f(A_1) \cap f(A_2),$$
$$(**) \qquad f^{-1}(B_1 \cap B_2) = f^{-1}(B_1) \cap f^{-1}(B_2).$$

These are simple logical facts, the establishment of which is immediate. That the equality sign does not always hold in (*) is shown, say, by the mapping $y = \sin x$ for the intervals A_1: $0 \leqq x \leqq 2\pi$ and A_2: $2\pi \leqq x \leqq 4\pi$. The equation (**) is thus so much the more remarkable. We note further the equality $f^{-1}(\complement B) = \complement f^{-1}(B)$ and point out the list of the fundamental set-theoretic equations and inclusions at the end of this little volume.

After these set-theoretic preliminaries, we now turn to the study of topological spaces.

5.1 Definition: Two topological spaces $\mathfrak{X}$ and $\mathfrak{Y}$ are said to be *homeomorphic* if there exists a one-to-one mapping f of $\mathfrak{X}$ onto $\mathfrak{Y}$ whereby the system $\mathfrak{D}_{\mathfrak{X}}$ of the open sets of $\mathfrak{X}$ correspond to the system

$\mathfrak{O}_{\mathfrak{Y}}$ of open sets of $\mathfrak{Y}$; f is called a *homeomorphic mapping* or a *homeomorphism* of $\mathfrak{X}$ onto $\mathfrak{Y}$.

Two homeomorphic spaces are therefore indistinguishable as topological structures; by means of f, the two topologies coincide completely. The concept of homeomorphism corresponds to the concept of isomorphism which one uses in dealing with algebraic structures, e.g. groups, rings, fields, and so on. The corresponding concept for metric spaces is that of an isometry.

5.2 Definition: Two metric spaces $\mathfrak{X}$ and $\mathfrak{Y}$, with metrics $d_{\mathfrak{X}}$ and $d_{\mathfrak{Y}}$ respectively, are said to be *isometric* if there exists a one-to-one mapping f of $\mathfrak{X}$ onto $\mathfrak{Y}$ such that $d_{\mathfrak{X}}(x, x') = d_{\mathfrak{Y}}(f(x), f(x'))$ for all x, $x' \in \mathfrak{X}$. The mapping f is called an *isometric mapping* of $\mathfrak{X}$ onto $\mathfrak{Y}$.

The concept of a continuous mapping which we will now introduce corresponds in many ways to the concept of a homomorphism for groups.

5.3 Definition: (Local Continuity): Let $f\colon \mathfrak{X} \to \mathfrak{Y}$ be a mapping of the topological space $\mathfrak{X}$ into the topological space $\mathfrak{Y}$ and let x be a point of $\mathfrak{X}$ and $y = f(x)$. Then f is said to be *continuous* at x if either one of the following two equivalent conditions is satisfied:

(1) For each neighborhood $V \in \mathfrak{U}(y)$ there exists a neighborhood $U \in \mathfrak{U}(x)$ such that $f(U) \subset V$.

(2) For each neighborhood $V \in \mathfrak{U}(y)$ we have that $f^{-1}(V) \in \mathfrak{U}(x)$.

Proof of equivalence. If (1) is satisfied, then $f^{-1}(V) \supset U$; since $U \in \mathfrak{U}(x)$, we also have that $f^{-1}(V) \in \mathfrak{U}(x)$ according to [U 2]. Conversely, if (2) is satisfied, then we choose $f^{-1}(V)$ to be that neighborhood whose existence is required in (1); we then certainly have that $f(f^{-1}(V)) \subset V$.

5.4 Definition: (Global Continuity): Let $f\colon \mathfrak{X} \to \mathfrak{Y}$ be a mapping of the topological space $\mathfrak{X}$ into the topological space $\mathfrak{Y}$. The mapping f is said to be *continuous*, or more precisely *continuous on* $\mathfrak{X}$, if any one of the following four equivalent conditions is satisfied:

(1) f is continuous for each $x \in \mathfrak{X}$.

(2) The pre-image set $f^{-1}(B)$ of each open set $B \subset \mathfrak{Y}$ is open.

(2′) The pre-image set $f^{-1}(C)$ of each closed set $C \subset \mathfrak{Y}$ is closed.

(3) For each set $A \subset \mathfrak{X}$, $f(\bar{A}) \subset \overline{f(A)}$ holds.

Moreover, a one-to-one mapping $f: \mathfrak{X} \to \mathfrak{Y}$ is homeomorphic if and only if, in analogy with the last condition (3), the following condition holds:

$$\text{for every set } A \subset \mathfrak{X}, f(\bar{A}) = \overline{f(A)}.$$

For, then not only is f continuous, because of (3), but also $f^{-1}: \mathfrak{Y} \to \mathfrak{X}$, inasmuch as for every set $B \subset \mathfrak{Y}$,

$$f^{-1}(\bar{B}) = f^{-1}(\overline{ff^{-1}(B)}) = f^{-1}(f(\overline{f^{-1}(B)})) = \overline{f^{-1}(B)}$$

holds.

Proof of the equivalence of conditions (1)–(3):

(1) $\Rightarrow$ (2). Let (1) be satisfied and $B \subset \mathfrak{Y}$ be open. Let y range over B, x range over $f^{-1}(y)$ for all y, i.e. x ranges over $f^{-1}(B)$. Then $B \in \mathfrak{U}(y)$ and therefore, according to (1), also $f^{-1}(B) \in \mathfrak{U}(x)$. Thus the set $f^{-1}(B)$ is a neighborhood of all its points and hence it is open.

(2) $\Rightarrow$ (1). Let (2) be satisfied, $x \in \mathfrak{X}$, $y = f(x)$. If $V \in \mathfrak{U}(y)$, then there exists an open set B such that $y \in B \subset V$. It follows that $x \in f^{-1}(B) \subset f^{-1}(V)$ with open $f^{-1}(B)$; thus, $f^{-1}(V) \in \mathfrak{U}(x)$.

(2) $\Leftrightarrow$ (2′). As B ranges over all open sets of $\mathfrak{Y}$, $\complement B$ ranges over all closed sets of $\mathfrak{Y}$. Then $f^{-1}(B)$ and $f^{-1}(\complement B)$ are complementary sets in $\mathfrak{X}$ (fundamental equation 9). Therefore, $f^{-1}(B)$ is open if, and only if, $f^{-1}(\complement B)$ is closed. This signifies the equivalence of (2) and (2′).

(2′) $\Rightarrow$ (3). Let f satisfy (2′). Let A be a subset of $\mathfrak{X}$ and p a contact point of A. It is to be proved that $f(\bar{A}) \subset \overline{f(A)}$ or that $f(p) \in \overline{f(A)}$. Now according to assumption (2′) $f^{-1}(\overline{f(A)})$ is closed; therefore, together with A also the contact point p belongs to $f^{-1}(\overline{f(A)})$. This means precisely that $f(p) \in \overline{f(A)}$.

(3) $\Rightarrow$ (2′). Let f satisfy (3). Let B be a closed subset of $\mathfrak{Y}$, p a contact point of $f^{-1}(B)$. It is to be shown that $f^{-1}(B)$ is closed or that $p \in f^{-1}(B)$. Now $f(p)$ is a contact point of $f(f^{-1}(B))$ according to assump-

tion (3). Since $f(f^{-1}(B)) \subset B$ (fundamental equation 10′), $f(p) \in B$, i.e. $p \in f^{-1}(B)$.

Conditions (2), (2′) are closely connected with the question whether the images of open sets are open and the images of closed sets are closed under a continuous mapping. That this is not the case in general is shown by the function $f(x) = \sin x$, which maps the open interval $0 < x < 2\pi$ of the x-axis onto the closed interval $-1 \leqq y \leqq +1$ of the y-axis (here the x-axis is the space $\mathfrak{X}$ and the y-axis is the space $\mathfrak{Y}$).

Further, the entire x-axis $R = R^1$, considered as a closed set, is mapped by means of the function $f(x) = \tanh x$ onto the non-closed interval $-1 < y < +1$ of the y-axis.

Continuous mappings which always map open sets of the original space $\mathfrak{X}$ into open sets of the image space are called *open mappings*; examples are formed by non-constant functions $f(z)$ of the complex variable z which are everywhere regular in a region $\mathscr{R}$ of the complex plane. *Closed mappings* are defined analogously; examples are formed by continuous mappings of a compact space $\mathfrak{X}$ into a Hausdorff space $\mathfrak{Y}$ (cf. Theorem 18.1, below). Both classes of mappings are of great significance for a more thorough theory of mappings.

If two mappings $f\colon \mathfrak{X} \to \mathfrak{Y}$ and $g\colon \mathfrak{Y} \to \mathfrak{Z}$ are given by the equations $y = f(x)$, $z = g(y)$, then the mapping $h\colon \mathfrak{X} \to \mathfrak{Z}$, which is defined by $z = g(f(x))$, is called the *composite mapping* or the *product mapping* $g \circ f = gf$. One must pay particular attention here to the order of the factors.

5.5 Theorem: *If the mappings $f\colon \mathfrak{X} \to \mathfrak{Y}$ and $g\colon \mathfrak{Y} \to \mathfrak{Z}$ are continuous, then the composite mapping $h = g \circ f\colon \mathfrak{X} \to \mathfrak{Z}$ is also continuous.*

Proof: Let $x \in \mathfrak{X}$, $f(x) = y$, $g(y) = z$. If $W \in \mathfrak{U}(z)$, then, by virtue of the continuity of g, the set $g^{-1}(W)$ is a neighborhood of y and, by virtue of the continuity of f, the set $f^{-1}(g^{-1}(W))$ is a neighborhood of x. Obviously, $f^{-1}(g^{-1}(W)) = h^{-1}(W)$.

5.6 Theorem: *A one-to-one mapping f of a topological space $\mathfrak{X}$ onto a topological space $\mathfrak{Y}$, for which f as well as f^{-1} are continuous, is a homeomorphism. Conversely, if f is a homeomorphism of $\mathfrak{X}$ onto $\mathfrak{Y}$, then f as well as f^{-1} are continuous.*

Proof: It must be shown that f and f^{-1} map the systems $\mathfrak{O}_{\mathfrak{X}}$ and $\mathfrak{O}_{\mathfrak{Y}}$ of the open sets of $\mathfrak{X}$ and $\mathfrak{Y}$ respectively into one another. On account of the continuity of f^{-1}, f maps the system $\mathfrak{O}_{\mathfrak{X}}$ into a subsystem of $\mathfrak{O}_{\mathfrak{Y}}$. If B is chosen arbitrarily from $\mathfrak{O}_{\mathfrak{Y}}$, then $f^{-1}(B) = A$ is open because f is continuous and $B = f(f^{-1}(B)) = f(A)$ is the image of the open set A from $\mathfrak{O}_{\mathfrak{X}}$. Therefore, f maps $\mathfrak{O}_{\mathfrak{X}}$ into the entire system $\mathfrak{O}_{\mathfrak{Y}}$, which is what was required to be proved. The converse is trivial.

We give yet an example of a one-to-one mapping f between two spaces $\mathfrak{X}$ and $\mathfrak{Y}$, in which f is continuous but f^{-1} is not continuous—hence f is not a homeomorphism. Let $\mathfrak{X}$ be the interval $0 \leqq t < 2\pi$ of the t-axis, $\mathfrak{Y}$ the unit circle in the (x, y)-plane R^2, $f(t) = (\cos t, \sin t)$; then f^{-1} is discontinuous at the point $(1, 0)$.

§ 6. Relative Topology

If $\mathfrak{X}$ is a metric space, S a subset of $\mathfrak{X}$, then one can consider S as a metric space, since certainly for each pair of points of S a distance is defined which satisfies axioms [M 1]–[M 3] of a metric space.

For topological spaces $\mathfrak{X}$, we apply the concept of trace to introduce a topology for a subset S of $\mathfrak{X}$. If $S \subset \mathfrak{X}$ is an arbitrary set, which is to be thought of as fixed, and if A ranges over arbitrary subsets of $\mathfrak{X}$, then

$$A_S = A \cap S$$

is called the *trace on* S of the set A. The following rules hold (cf. fundamental formulas (4), (4′)):

$$(A \cup B)_S = A_S \cup B_S, \; (A \cap B)_S = A_S \cap B_S,$$

which one can verify directly; the corresponding rules for an arbitrary number of factors also hold.

6.1 Theorem: *A topology $\mathfrak{T}_S$ is defined in a subset S of the topological space $\mathfrak{X}$ with the topology $\mathfrak{T}$ by taking the open sets of S to be the traces A_S on S of the open sets A of $\mathfrak{X}$.*

Proof: Let $\mathfrak{D} = \{A_\lambda \mid \lambda$ from an arbitrary index set $\Lambda\}$ be the system of open sets of $\mathfrak{T}$. Let $\mathfrak{D}_S$ be the system of the traces $B_\lambda = (A_\lambda)_S = A_\lambda \cap S$. It must be shown that $\mathfrak{D}_S$ satisfies the axioms [O 1] and [O 2]. In fact,

$$\bigcup B_\lambda = \bigcup (A_\lambda)_S = (\bigcup A_\lambda)_S = A_S$$

as λ ranges over Λ, where A is an open set of $\mathfrak{X}$. [O 1] follows from this. [O 2] is obtained in an entirely analogous way.

6.2 Definition: The topology $\mathfrak{T}_S$ defined in Theorem 6.1 is called the *trace topology* $\mathfrak{T}_S$ of $\mathfrak{T}$ on S or the *topology induced* in S by $\mathfrak{T}$ or also the *relative topology* for S; S is called a *subspace* of $\mathfrak{X}$.

If $A \subset \mathfrak{X}$, then $\complement A = \mathfrak{X} - A$ denotes the complement in $\mathfrak{X}$; on the other hand, if $B \subset S$, then $\complement_S B = S - B$ denotes the complement in S. Then the rule $(\complement A)_S = \complement_S A_S$ (fundamental formula (5)) holds. It follows from this rule that the closed sets of $\mathfrak{T}_S$ are identical with the traces of the closed sets of $\mathfrak{T}$. One must pay special attention to the fact that the concepts "open," closed," "interior," and so forth, are meaningful only with respect to a given topology; therefore, one must always say "open in $\mathfrak{T}_S$" or "open in S," and so on, whenever there is danger of confusion. We make use of the abbreviated terminology "S-open," "S-interior," and so on. It is not always true that an S-open subset B of S is always $\mathfrak{X}$-open, as one can easily verify with very simple examples. Moreover, the following theorem holds.

6.3 Theorem: *If S is a subspace of the topological space $\mathfrak{X}$, then: All S-open subsets of S are also $\mathfrak{X}$-open if, and only if, S is open in $\mathfrak{X}$. This theorem remains true when one replaces the word "open" by "closed."*

Proof: If S is $\mathfrak{X}$-open, then $A_S = A \cap S$ is also $\mathfrak{X}$-open whenever A is. Conversely, if the traces A_S of all the $\mathfrak{X}$-open sets A are $\mathfrak{X}$-open, then in particular $\mathfrak{X}_S = S$ is $\mathfrak{X}$-open.

We shall describe in the next theorem the S-neighborhoods of the points $p \in S$ by means of their $\mathfrak{X}$-neighborhoods.

6.4 Theorem: *The S-neighborhoods of a point $p \in S$ are identical with the traces of the $\mathfrak{X}$-neighborhoods of p.*

Proof: If $U \in \mathfrak{U}(p)$ in $\mathfrak{X}$, $p \in S$, then there exists an $\mathfrak{X}$-open set O with $p \in O \subset U$. By means of trace formation, it follows that $p \in O_S \subset U_S$, O_S is S-open, and therefore U_S is an S-neighborhood of p. If V is an S-neighborhood of $p \in S$, then $p \in B \subset V$ for a suitable S-open set $B \subset S$. We have that $B = O_S$ for some $\mathfrak{X}$-open set O, and hence $p \in O \subset (O \cup V)$. $O \cup V$ is an $\mathfrak{X}$-neighborhood of p and has the trace $(O \cup V)_S = O_S \cup V_S = B \cup V = V$. This completes the proof of the theorem.

One might think that the interior and closure under the formation of the relative topology have behavior analogous to that of the concepts "open," "closed," and "neighborhood." In fact, the following proposition holds: If $A \subset S$, then the S-closure of A is equal to the trace in S of the $\mathfrak{X}$-closure of A. But by no means does a corresponding theorem hold for the S-interiors as one can make clear with the simplest examples.

§ 7. Connectedness

7.1 Definition: A topological space is said to be *connected* if it does not allow a partition into two non-empty open subsets.

Concerning the concept of *partition*, consult the index. The condition of the definition is equivalent to each of the following five conditions:

(1) There do not exist subsets A and B of $\mathfrak{X}$ with the properties: $A \neq \emptyset$, $B \neq \emptyset$, A and B open, $\mathfrak{X} = A \cup B$, $A \cap B = \emptyset$.

(2) If the subsets A and B of $\mathfrak{X}$ are non-empty and open and $\mathfrak{X} = A \cup B$, then $A \cap B \neq \emptyset$.

(3) If the subsets A and B of $\mathfrak{X}$ are open and $\mathfrak{X} = A \cup B$, $A \cap B = \emptyset$, then $A = \mathfrak{X}$ and $B = \emptyset$ or $A = \emptyset$ and $B = \mathfrak{X}$.

(4) In Definition 7.1 and in the criteria (1)–(3), one can replace the word "open" by the word "closed."

(5) There exists no open-closed subsets A of $\mathfrak{X}$ except $\emptyset$ and $\mathfrak{X}$.

(1) is only a detailed form of Definition 7.1. (2) and (3) are formal

reversals of (1), (4) is equivalent with (1) inasmuch as in (1) $A = \complement B$ and likewise $B = \complement A$ are open-closed. (5) holds for the same reason.

Examples: (a) The space $\mathfrak{X}$ which consists of two disjoint circular surfaces in the Euclidean plane (with the relative topology, induced from the plane) is not connected.

(b) The rational line Q (with the relative topology) is not connected because the set A of all rational points $< \sqrt{2}$ is open-closed.

(c) The real line $R = R^1$ as well as any open or closed interval $I \subset R$ (with the relative topology) is connected.

Proof of (c): Assume that $A \neq \varnothing, \neq \mathfrak{X}$ is an open-closed subset of $\mathfrak{X}$. Then there exist points $a \in A$ and $b \in \complement A$ since $\mathfrak{X}$ contains more than one point. Let, say, $a < b$. Then the least upper bound of the set $A_0 = \{x \mid x \in A, x < a\}$ is a finite real numer c, $a \leqq c \leqq b$. We have that $c \in A$ since A is closed. An entire neighborhood of c belongs to A since A is open. Hence a neighborhood of c also belongs to A_0, contrary to the definition of the least upper bound of A_0. Therefore, a set A of the sort assumed cannot exist and so $\mathfrak{X}$ is connected.

7.2 Definition: A subset C of $\mathfrak{X}$ is called *connected* if C, considered as a subspace, is connected. An open connected subset is called a *region*.

7.3 Theorem: *C is connected if, and only if, any one of the following two conditions is satisfied:*

(1′) *There do not exist subsets A, B, of $\mathfrak{X}$ with the properties that $A \cap C \neq \varnothing$, $B \cap C \neq \varnothing$, A, B open (in $\mathfrak{X}$), $C \subset A \cup B$, $A \cap B \cap C = \varnothing$.*

(3′) *If the subsets A and B of $\mathfrak{X}$ are open and $C \subset A \cup B$, $A \cap B \cap C = \varnothing$,* then it follows that $C \subset A$, $B \cap C = \varnothing$ or $A \cap C = \varnothing$, $C \subset B$.

One can also replace in (1′) *and* (3′) *the word "open" by the word "closed."*

Proof: Again, (3′) is simply the formal converse of (1′); the interchange of "open" and "closed" is obtained as just above. We shall prove (3′): Let C be connected. If A and B are open subsets of $\mathfrak{X}$ in the sense of (3′) with $C \subset A \cup B$, $A \cap B \cap C = \varnothing$, then the traces $A_C = A \cap C$ and $B_C = B \cap C$ satisfy the assumption of condition (3), applied to the space C. Therefore, according to (3), $A_C = \emptyset$ or $B_C = \emptyset$, and this is what is to be proved in (3′).

Conversely, let (3′) be satisfied. In the space C, let A' and B' be C-open in the sense of (3), with $C = A' \cup B'$, $A' \cap B' = \emptyset$. Then A' and B' are traces of open sets A and B from $\mathfrak{X}$, $A' = A \cap C$, $B' = B \cap C$. A and B satisfy the assumptions of condition (3′); therefore, we have either $A \cap C = \emptyset$ or $B \cap C = \emptyset$, and hence $A' = \emptyset$ or $B' = \emptyset$, as is required in (3).

7.4 Theorem: *If $f: \mathfrak{X} \to \mathfrak{X}'$ is a continuous mapping and C is a connected subset of $\mathfrak{X}$, then $C' = f(C)$ is also connected.*

Proof: Let A' and B' be open subsets of $\mathfrak{X}'$ in the sense of (3′) with $C' \subset A' \cup B'$, $A' \cap B' \cap C' = \emptyset$. Then $f^{-1}(A') = A$, $f^{-1}(B') = B$ are open subsets of $\mathfrak{X}$ with $C \subset A \cup B$, $A \cap B \cap C = \emptyset$. According to (3′) for the space C it follows that $C \subset A$ or $C \subset B$, and therefore either $C' \subset A'$ or $C' \subset B'$, which is what had to be proved.

7.5 Theorem: *If $\{C_\lambda\}$ (λ from an arbitrary index set Λ) are connected subsets of $\mathfrak{X}$ such that $C_{\lambda'} \cap C_{\lambda''} \neq \emptyset$ for $\lambda' \neq \lambda''$, then the union $C = \bigcup C_\lambda$ is also connected.*

Proof: Let A and B be open subsets of $\mathfrak{X}$ in the sense of (3′) with $C \subset A \cup B$, $A \cap B \cap C = \emptyset$. Then *a fortiori* we have $C_1 \subset A \cup B$ and $A \cap B \cap C_1 = \emptyset$; the assumption of (3′) therefore holds for C_1, and hence $C_1 \subset A$ or $C_1 \subset B$. Let, say, $C_1 \subset A$. Analogously, one concludes that $C_\lambda \subset A$ or $C_\lambda \subset B$. Of these two possibilities, only the first one, $C_\lambda \subset A$, comes into consideration since $C_1 \cap C_\lambda \neq \emptyset$ and $A \cap B \cap C = \emptyset$. Since this holds for all λ, (3′) follows, i.e. C is connected.

According to this, a convex set C in R^n, for example, is connected; for, an arbitrarily chosen fixed point $p \in C$ can be joined by a polygonal arc with every point $x \in C$, and a polygonal arc is, according to example (c), connected.

7.6 Theorem: *If C is a connected subset of $\mathfrak{X}$, $C \subset D \subset \bar{C}$, then D is also connected.*

Proof: We apply (3′) in the formulation for closed A, B. Let A, B be closed subsets of $\mathfrak{X}$ with $D \subset A \cup B$, $A \cap B \cap D = \varnothing$. Then we have *a fortiori* that $C \subset A \cup B$, $A \cap B \cap C = \varnothing$. It follows according to (3′), say, that $C \subset A$. It follows further that $D \subset \bar{C} \subset \bar{A} = A$, and therefore $D \subset A$. According to (3′), this shows that D is connected.

As an example for this theorem, we consider the set A of all points (x, y) of the plane R^2 with $0 < x \leqq 1$ and $y = \sin(1/x)$. $\bar{A}$ arises from A by the adjunction of the set A_0 of all $(0, y)$ with $-1 \leqq y \leqq +1$. If A_0' is an arbitrary subset of A_0, then, according to the theorem, $A \cup A_0'$ is also connected.

7.7 Theorem: *If C is connected, D an arbitrary subset of $\mathfrak{X}$ and C intersects D as well as $\complement D$, then C also intersects the boundary ϱD.*

Proof: Assume that $C \cap \varrho D = \varnothing$. Since $\mathfrak{X} = \underline{D} \cup \underline{\complement D} \cup \varrho D$, then the open sets $A = \underline{D}$, $B = \underline{\complement D}$ would have the properties that $C \subset A \cup B$, $C \cap A \cap B = \varnothing$. Since, moreover, according to assumption, $C \cap A = C \cap \underline{D} = C \cap D \neq \varnothing$, and $C \cap B \neq \varnothing$, C would not be connected, according to Theorem 7.3 (1′), contrary to our assumption. This completes the proof of the theorem.

7.8 Theorem: *If $\mathfrak{X}$ is connected and D is a subset of $\mathfrak{X}$ which is distinct from $\varnothing$ and $\mathfrak{X}$, then $\varrho D \neq \varnothing$.*

The proof follows from the preceding theorem if we identify the set C occurring there with $\mathfrak{X}$.

Let $\mathfrak{X}$ be an arbitrary topological space. If we define two points x, $y \in \mathfrak{X}$ to be equivalent if x and y are contained in one connected subset C of $\mathfrak{X}$, then this defines a reflexive, symmetric and transitive relation among the points of $\mathfrak{X}$. Transitivity is verified as follows: If x and y are contained in the connected set C, y and z in the connected set D, then x and z are contained in the set $C \cup D$, which, according to Theorem 7.5, is connected. The equivalence classes, relative to this equivalence relation, are called the *connectivity components*, or briefly the *components*, of $\mathfrak{X}$. A component C of $\mathfrak{X}$ is therefore a maximal connected subset of $\mathfrak{X}$. The component $C(x)$ of a point $x \in \mathfrak{X}$, the set of all those points of $\mathfrak{X}$ which together with x lie in a connected subset of $\mathfrak{X}$, can also be defined as the largest connected subset of $\mathfrak{X}$ containing x. Every open-closed subset of $\mathfrak{X}$, which contains the point x, contains the entire component $C(x)$ as a subset. Theorem 7.6 implies the next theorem.

7.9 Theorem: *The components of a topological space are closed sets.*

Moreover, components in general are not open, as, for instance, example (b) at the beginning of this section shows. We conclude with the following definition.

7.10 Definition: A space is called *totally disconnected* if each of its components consists of one point.

§ 8. Connectedness of Point Sets in R^n

Special assertions can be made about the connectedness of subsets in Euclidean space R^n. We first consider connected sets on the real line R^1. To them belong, as we saw, the intervals and indeed the open intervals $(a, b) = \{x \mid a < x < b\}$, the closed intervals $[a, b] = \{x \mid a \leqq x \leqq b\}$ and the half-open intervals, e.g., $[a, b) = \{x \mid a \leqq x < b\}$. Among the open intervals we also count the sets $(-\infty, b) = \{x \mid x < b\}$, $(a, +\infty) = \{x \mid x > a\}$ and $(-\infty, +\infty) = R^1$. Now the following theorem is valid.

8.1 Theorem: *The only connected sets in R^1 are the one-point sets and arbitrary intervals. The only regions are the open intervals.*

Proof: Let C be a connected set in R^1.

(1) Let $x_1, x_2 \in C$ and $y \in (x_1, x_2)$. If we had $y \notin C$, then the sets $A = \{x \mid x \in C, x < y\}$ and $B = \{x \mid x \in C, x > y\}$ would form a partition of C into two non-empty open subsets, which, according to the definition of connectedness, do not exist. Therefore, together with each pair of points $x_1, x_2 \in C$, the entire interval $[x_1, x_2]$ belongs to C.

(2) Let $a = \inf C$, $b = \sup C$, $a < b$ and $x \in (a, b)$. According to the definition of inf and sup, there exist $x_1, x_2 \in C$ with $a \leqq x_1 < x < x_2 \leqq$

b; according to (1), it follows that $x \in C$. It should be clear how these inequalities are meant if $a = -\infty$ or $b = +\infty$. Therefore, $C = (a, b)$ or $= [a, b]$ or $= (a, b]$ or $= [a, b)$, which is what was to be proved.

By a *polygonal arc* in Euclidean space R^n with the vertices $x_0, \ldots, x_m$ we understand the union of the finitely many segments $[x_{i-1}, x_i]$ for $i = 1, \ldots, m$. Here, we allow the segments to overlap. We say that x_0 and x_m are *joined* by the polygonal arc.

8.2 Theorem: *An open set O in R^n is connected if, and only if, any pair of its points can be joined by a polygonal arc in O.*

Proof: A polygonal arc is a connected set as one recognizes by applying Theorem 7.5 a finite number of times. If every pair of points of O can be joined by a polygonal arc in O, then, according to Theorem 7.5, O is connected.

Conversely, now let O be connected. Let $a \in O$ and C be the set of all $x \in O$ which can be joined to a by a polygonal arc. C is connected and nonempty. When we show that C is open-closed in O, it will follow from this according to Definition 7.1, (5) that $C = O$; and therefore the theorem holds. We shall first prove that C is open: Let $x \in C$ be joinable with a by a polygonal arc. Since O is open, there exists an ε-neighborhood U of x which is contained in O. Every point $y \in U$ is joinable with x by a rectilinear segment and hence with a by a polygonal arc, and therefore it belongs to C, and this proves the assertion. We show further that C is closed: If $y \in O$ is a contact point of C, then there exist points $x \in C$ in every ε-neighborhood $U \subset O$ of y. y is joinable with x by a rectilinear segment, and x is joinable with a by a polygonal arc; therefore y is also joinable with a by a polygonal arc, i.e. $y \in C$. This proves that C is closed and completes the proof of the theorem.

If instead of starting in the preceding discussion with the concept of a polygonal arc one starts with the concept of a *simple polygonal arc* in which the above-named segments $[x_{i-1}, x_i]$ do not intersect (except at their endpoints), then Theorem 8.2 remains valid without modification; its proof offers no fundamental difficulties.

8.3 Theorem: *The components of an open set in R^n are open and hence they are regions.*

Proof: Let the set C be a component of the open set O, $x \in C$. Then an ε-neighborhood U of x likewise belongs to O. U is connected and has points in common with the connected set C. Therefore $C \cup U$ is connected and, because of the maximality property of C, it follows that $U \subset C$. Therefore x is an interior point of C and so C is open.

In particular, according to this and by Theorem 8.1, the components of an open set in R^1 are open intervals. The representation of an open set O in R^1 as the union of disjoint open intervals, as was stated in Theorem 3.13, is therefore nothing else than the decomposition of the set O into its components; this decomposition is unique.

8.4 Theorem: *An open set in R^n is the union of at most a denumerable number of regions.*

This generalization of Theorem 3.13 follows immediately from the last theorem.

§ 9. Density

9.1 Definition: A subset A of the space $\mathfrak{X}$ is said to be *dense in* $\mathfrak{X}$ (also *everywhere dense in* $\mathfrak{X}$) when either one of the following two equivalent conditions is satisfied: (1) $\overline{A} = \mathfrak{X}$, (2) every non-empty open subset of $\mathfrak{X}$ contains points of A.

The equivalence of the two conditions is almost self-evident: Both mean that every neighborhood of a point of $\mathfrak{X}$ contains points of A. For example, the set A of rational points on the real line R^1 is dense. The same statement holds for the set of irrational points. Therefore A as well as $\complement A$ can be dense in $\mathfrak{X}$. If A is dense in $\mathfrak{X}$, then every subset A' of $\mathfrak{X}$ such that $A' \supset A$ is dense in $\mathfrak{X}$.

9.2 Definition: A subset A of the space $\mathfrak{X}$ is said to be *nowhere dense* in $\mathfrak{X}$ if either one of the following two equivalent conditions is satisfied:

(1′) $\overline{A}$ has no interior points;

(2′) For each non-empty open subset O of $\mathfrak{X}$ there exists a non-empty open set $O_1 \subset O$ with $O_1 \cap A = \emptyset$.

Proof of equivalence: Let (1′) be satisfied and let O be a non-empty open subset of $\mathfrak{X}$. If there were points of A in every non-empty open set $O_1 \subset O$, then we should have $O \subset \overline{A}$, contrary to (1′).

Conversely, let (2′) be satisfied. If x is an arbitrary point in $\mathfrak{X}$ and U an open neighborhood of x, then there exists a non-empty open set $O_1 \subset U$ which belongs entirely to $\complement A$. Since the points of O_1 do not belong to A, x is not an interior point of A.

For example, a line is nowhere dense in R^2. If A is nowhere dense in $\mathfrak{X}$, then $\bar{A}$ is also. (1) and (1′) show that a set cannot be simultaneously dense and nowhere dense in $\mathfrak{X}$. If A is nowhere dense in $\mathfrak{X}$, then $\complement A$ is dense in $\mathfrak{X}$, as follows directly from (2′). The converse does not hold as our preceding examples show. On the other hand, one can make the following assertion.

9.3 Theorem: *A closed set A is nowhere dense in $\mathfrak{X}$ if, and only if, $\complement A$ is dense in $\mathfrak{X}$.*

Proof: For closed sets A, (1′) means that A has no interior points, that therefore $\underline{A} = \emptyset$. Because $\overline{\complement A} = \complement \underline{A}$, this is equivalent to $\overline{\complement A} = \mathfrak{X}$.

In the sequel, we shall give an example of a totally disconnected set which is nowhere dense on the real line R^1 and which is of fundamental significance for many topological investigations—this is the so-called *Cantor discontinuum* $\mathscr{C}$. It is constructed as follows: In the closed "C-interval of zero rank" $C = [0, 1]$ we delete after trisection the open "B-interval of zero rank" $B = \left(\frac{1}{3}, \frac{2}{3}\right)$ so that the two closed C-intervals of the first rank $C_0 = \left[0, \frac{1}{3}\right]$ and $C_1 = \left[\frac{2}{3}, 1\right]$ remain. From C_0 and C_1, we delete after trisection the open B-intervals of the first rank $B_0 = \left(\frac{1}{9}, \frac{2}{9}\right)$ and $B_1 = \left(\frac{7}{9}, \frac{8}{9}\right)$ respectively, so that the closed C-intervals of the second rank $C_{00} = \left[0, \frac{1}{9}\right]$, $C_{01} = \left[\frac{2}{9}, \frac{3}{9}\right]$, $C_{10} = \left[\frac{6}{9}, \frac{7}{9}\right]$, and $C_{11} = \left[\frac{8}{9}, 1\right]$ remain.

We continue this process analogously: If one has already constructed 2^{n-1} closed C-intervals of the $(n - 1)$-st rank $C_{i_1 i_2 \ldots i_{n-1}}$ $(i_1, \ldots, i_{n-1} = 0$ or $1)$, then we delete from each $C_{i_1 \ldots i_{n-1}}$ by trisection the open B-interval of the $(n - 1)$-st rank $B_{i_1 \ldots i_{n-1}}$ so that the two closed C-intervals of the n-th rank $C_{i_1 \ldots i_{n-1} 0}$ and $C_{i_1 \ldots i_{n-1} 1}$ remain. For each $n = 0, 1, 2, \ldots$, one thus obtains 2^n closed C-intervals of the n-th rank $C_{i_1 \ldots i_n}$ of length $\frac{1}{3^n}$, which are separated from one another by the open B-intervals which have a rank $< n$; their length is $\geqq \frac{1}{3^n}$. Every subinterval of $[0, 1]$ with a length $> \frac{1}{3^n}$ therefore contains points from B-intervals of rank $< n$.

Now let $C^{(n)}$ be the union of all C-intervals of the n-th rank, $B^{(n)} = [0, 1] - C^{(n)}$ the union of all B-intervals of all ranks $< n$. $C^{(n)}$ is closed, $B^{(n)}$ is open; each of the intervals on [0, 1] having length $> \frac{1}{3^n}$ contains points of $B^{(n)}$. We form

$$\mathscr{C} = \bigcap_{n=0}^{\infty} C^{(n)} = [0, 1] - \bigcup_{n=0}^{\infty} B^{(n)}.$$

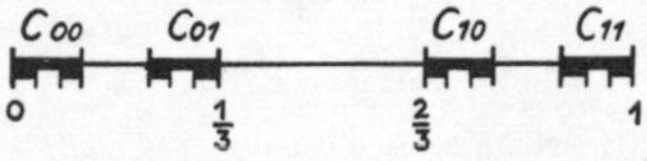

Fig. 2

This set is the Cantor discontinuum $\mathscr{C}$. We shall prove that $\mathscr{C}$ has the following six properties: (1) $\mathscr{C}$ is closed, and therefore compact in the sense of Chapter 5. (2) The endpoints of all the B-intervals including the points 0 and 1 form a set $\mathscr{C}_1$. We have that $\mathscr{C}_1 \subset \mathscr{C}$ since in the construction process of $\mathscr{C}$ the points of $\mathscr{C}_1$ are never deleted. They are called points of the first type of $\mathscr{C}$. The remaining points of $\mathscr{C}$ are called points of the second type; they form the set $\mathscr{C}_2$; we have that $\mathscr{C} = \mathscr{C}_1 \cup \mathscr{C}_2$. (3) Every point p of $\mathscr{C}$ is an accumulation point of $\mathscr{C}$, even more, an accumulation point of $\mathscr{C}_1$. For, p lies in a C-interval of the n-th rank and hence has points of the first type arbitrarily close to it. (4) To each $p \in \mathscr{C}$ there corresponds a uniquely determined sequence

$$C \supset C_{i_1} \supset C_{i_1 i_2} \supset C_{i_1 i_2 i_3} \supset \ldots$$

of C-intervals all of which contain p. So, p arises from a uniquely determined sequence $i_1\, i_2\, i_3 \ldots$, where $i_j = 0$ or 1. Conversely, to each such sequence there corresponds a uniquely determined point $p \in \mathscr{C}$. Therefore $\mathscr{C}$ is related in a one-to-one fashion with the set of all these sequences, and, since this set has the cardinality $\mathfrak{c}$ of the continuum, $\mathscr{C}$ also has this cardinality. Since $\mathscr{C}_1$ is denumerable, it follows from this, in particular, that $\mathscr{C}_2$ is non-empty and moreover it has the cardinality $\mathfrak{c}$. (5) $\mathscr{C}$ is nowhere dense in [0, 1] because every open interval of [0, 1] (hence every open set) contains points of $B^{(n)}$ when n is so large that $\frac{1}{3^n}$ is smaller than the length of the interval. (6) $\mathscr{C}$ is zero-dimensional, by which the following is understood (cf. §§ 32, 33): For each real $\varepsilon > 0$, $\mathscr{C}$ is representable as the union of a finite number of disjoint closed subsets in C of diameter

$< \varepsilon$. Obviously, the sets $\mathscr{C} \cap C_{i_1 \ldots i_n}$ form such subsets and indeed of diameter $\leqq \frac{1}{3^n}$ when the $C_{i_1 \ldots i_n}$ range over all C-intervals of the n-th rank. We note without proof that one can define $\mathscr{C}$ in an especially simple way as the set of all those real numbers α which can be written as triadic fractions $\alpha = 0.\nu_1 \nu_2 \ldots$, which require only the digits 0 and 2 but not the digit 1.

Chapter 3

RELATIONSHIP OF VARIOUS TOPOLOGIES TO ONE ANOTHER

§ 10. Bases

A topology $\mathfrak{T}$ for a set $\mathfrak{X}$ is completely determined by the system $\mathfrak{O}$ of the open sets or by the systems $\mathfrak{U}(p)$ of neighborhoods of the points p. Conversely, these systems are uniquely determined by $\mathfrak{T}$. For many purposes, in particular for the construction of topologies for a given set, it is desirable to describe $\mathfrak{T}$ by means of less comprehensive systems which might not be uniquely determined by $\mathfrak{T}$. This occurs in the case of space bases and neighborhood bases, which we shall now introduce.

10.1 Definition: A system $\mathfrak{B} = \{B_\lambda \mid \lambda$ from an arbitrary index set $\Lambda\}$ of open sets B_λ of the topological space $\mathfrak{X}$ is called a *basis of* $\mathfrak{X}$ or a *basis of* $\mathfrak{T}$ if each open set of $\mathfrak{X}$ is the union of elements from $\mathfrak{B}$.

We point out that we include $\varnothing$ in every case as a union (see the index); therefore, $\varnothing$ need not occur in $\mathfrak{B}$.

Examples: (a) $\mathfrak{O}$ itself is a basis of $\mathfrak{X}$. (b) In a metric space $\mathfrak{X}$, the totality of all spherical neighborhoods of all points of $\mathfrak{X}$ form a basis. Namely, if O is an open set in $\mathfrak{X}$, $x \in O$, then there exists a neighborhood $U_x = \mathfrak{U}_\varepsilon(x)$ such that $x \in U_x \subset O$. Then $O = \bigcup U_x$ taken over all $x \in O$. (c) In R^n the spherical neighborhoods with rational radii about rational points (i.e. those with rational coordinates) form a basis. Namely, if O is an open set in R^n, $x \in O$, then there exists a spherical neighborhood $\mathfrak{U}_{2\varepsilon}(x)$ with rational radius 2ε about x, which lies entirely in O. Then surely a rational point a lies in $\mathfrak{U}_\varepsilon(x)$ and for $V_x = \mathfrak{U}_\varepsilon(a)$ we have that $x \in V_x \subset O$. Then $O = \bigcup V_x$, taken over all $x \in O$. Since the set of rational points in R^n and thereby also the set of spheres with rational radii about these points is denumerable, one can say: R^n possesses a denumerable basis. (d) One can easily show that also the Hilbert space H possesses a denumerable basis. One takes, say, all spherical neighborhoods with rational radii about the points of the form $(r_1, \ldots, r_n, 0, 0, \ldots)$ with rational $r_1, \ldots, r_n$.

10.2 Theorem: *In a given topological space* $\mathfrak{X}$, *let* $\mathfrak{B} = \{B_\lambda \mid \lambda$ *from an arbitrary index set* $\Lambda\}$ *be a system of open sets.* $\mathfrak{B}$ *is a basis of* $\mathfrak{X}$ *if, and only if, to each open set* $O \subset \mathfrak{X}$ *and to each point* $p \in O$ *there exists a* $B_\lambda \in \mathfrak{B}$ *such that* $p \in B_\lambda \subset O$.

Proof: First, let $\mathfrak{B}$ be a basis of $\mathfrak{X}$. If O is open, $p \in O$, then O is, according to the definition, the union of certain $B_\lambda \in \mathfrak{B}$; at least one of these sets B_λ must contain p, $p \in B_\lambda \subset O$. Conversely, let the condition of the theorem be satisfied and let O be an open subset of $\mathfrak{X}$. For each $p \in O$ there exists a $B_\lambda = B_\lambda(p)$ with $p \in B_\lambda \subset O$. Then obviously $O = \bigcup B_\lambda(p)$, where the union is taken over all $p \in O$. Thus, $\mathfrak{B}$ is a basis.

10.3 Definition: A system $\mathfrak{V}(p)$ of neighborhoods of a point p in the topological space $\mathfrak{X}$ is called a *neighborhood basis of* p (also a *fundamental system of neighborhoods of* p) if to each neighborhood $U \in \mathfrak{U}(p)$ there exists a $V \in \mathfrak{V}(p)$ such that $V \subset U$. If $\mathfrak{V}(p)$ consists of open neighborhoods only, then $\mathfrak{V}(p)$ is called an *open* neighborhood basis of p. A *closed* neighborhood basis is defined in a corresponding manner.

Examples: (a) $\mathfrak{U}(p)$ itself is a neighborhood basis of p. (b) The spherical neighborhoods of a point of a metric space form an open neighborhood basis of p.

The following theorem shows that there always exist open neighborhood bases; the existence of closed neighborhood bases is, however, assured only for special classes of spaces, as we shall see later.

10.4 Theorem: *Those sets B_λ of a basis $\mathfrak{B} = \{B_\lambda \mid \lambda$ from an arbitrary index set $\Lambda\}$ of the topological space $\mathfrak{X}$, which contain a fixed point p, form an open neighborhood basis of p. If for each point $p \in \mathfrak{X}$ the system $\mathfrak{V}(p)$ is an open neighborhood basis, then $\mathfrak{B} = \bigcup \mathfrak{V}(p)$, taken over all $p \in \mathfrak{X}$, is a basis of $\mathfrak{X}$.*

Proof: If $U \in \mathfrak{U}(p)$, then there exists an open set O such that $p \in O \subset U$ (Theorem 3.4). O is the union of sets from $\mathfrak{B}$; at least one of them, say B_λ, contains p. Then we have that $p \in B_\lambda \subset U$. Therefore U contains an element of $\mathfrak{V}(p)$, which was first to be shown.

If O is an open set of $\mathfrak{X}$, $p \in O$, then there exists by assumption an open set $B_p \in \mathfrak{V}(p)$ such that $p \in B_p \subset O$. Thus $\bigcup \mathfrak{V}(p)$ is proved to be a basis according to Theorem 10.2.

After having considered bases of a given topological space $\mathfrak{X}$, we now ask under what conditions is a system of subsets of a set $\mathfrak{X}$ suitable for a basis of a topology over $\mathfrak{X}$. In this connection, the following theorem is valid.

10.5 Theorem: *In a set $\mathfrak{X}$, let a system $\mathfrak{B} = \{B_\lambda \mid \lambda$ from an arbitrary index set $\Lambda\}$ of subsets be given with the property that: If B_λ, $B_{\lambda'} \in \mathfrak{B}$ and if $p \in B_\lambda \cap B_{\lambda'}$, then there exists a $B_\mu \in \mathfrak{B}$ such that $p \in B_\mu \subset B_\lambda \cap B_{\lambda'}$; moreover, assume $\mathfrak{X} = \bigcup_{\lambda \in \Lambda} B_\lambda$. Then there exists precisely one topology $\mathfrak{T}$ for $\mathfrak{X}$ in which $\mathfrak{B}$ is a basis of $\mathfrak{T}$.*

Proof: Let $\mathfrak{O}$ be the system of all unions of sets B_λ, including $\emptyset$. If there exists a topology of the required sort, then $\mathfrak{O}$ must be the system of the open sets of $\mathfrak{T}$. Therefore there exists at most one topology $\mathfrak{T}$ of the required sort. On the other hand, $\mathfrak{O}$ actually satisfies axioms [O 1] and [O 2]; it therefore really defines a topology $\mathfrak{T}$. This is clear for [O 1]. In order to also prove [O 2], we choose $O_1, O_2 \in \mathfrak{O}$. If $O_1 \cap O_2 = \emptyset$, then $O_1 \cap O_2$ is in $\mathfrak{O}$. If $O_1 \cap O_2 \neq \emptyset$, then let $p \in O_1 \cap O_2$. Since O_1, O_2 are unions of B_λ, there exist B_1, $B_2 \in \mathfrak{B}$ such that $p \in B_1 \subset O_1$, $p \in B_2 \subset O_2$. Hence there exists a $B_\mu = B_\mu(p) \in \mathfrak{B}$ such that $p \in B_\mu \subset B_1 \cap B_2$. Clearly, $O_1 \cap O_2 = \bigcup B_\mu(p)$, taken over all $p \in O_1 \cap O_2$, which proves that $O_1 \cap O_2 \in \mathfrak{O}$. Since also $\mathfrak{X} \in \mathfrak{O}$, this proves [$O$ 2].

Without going further into the various bases of a topological space $\mathfrak{X}$, we remark yet that the smallest of the cardinalities of these bases is called the *weight* of the space $\mathfrak{X}$; such a smallest cardinality exists since the set of cardinal numbers is well ordered (cf. E. KAMKE [1], § 44, Theorem 3). Only the case of denumerable weights will still be treated briefly.

10.6 Theorem: *If the topological space $\mathfrak{X}$ possesses a denumerable basis, then there exists in $\mathfrak{X}$ a denumerable dense point set.*

Proof: If $\mathfrak{B} = \{B_i \mid i = 1, 2, \ldots\}$ is a denumerable basis of $\mathfrak{X}$, then we choose in each B_i a point p_i. The denumerable set of the p_i is then dense in $\mathfrak{X}$: Namely, if O is open, then there exists a $B_i \subset O$ and hence $p_i \in O$.

10.7 Theorem: *A metric space $\mathfrak{X}$ possesses a denumerable basis if, and only if, there exists a denumerable dense set in $\mathfrak{X}$.*

Proof: Taking the preceding theorem into consideration, we must yet show only that in a metric space the existence of a denumerable dense set implies the existence of a denumerable basis. This verification is carried out literally as in the proof of example (*c*) at the end of Definition 10.1.

10.8 Theorem: *In a topological space $\mathfrak{X}$ with denumerable basis, the system of open sets and likewise the system of the closed sets has at most the cardinality $\mathfrak{c}$ of the continuum.*

Proof: Let $\mathfrak{B} = \{B_i \mid i = 1, 2, \ldots\}$ be a denumerable basis of $\mathfrak{X}$. Each open set $O \subset \mathfrak{X}$ is the union of certain sets B_i and therefore O determines, by means of the corresponding indices i, a subset of natural numbers. Distinct open sets obviously determine distinct subsets of this sort. The system of all open sets is therefore equivalent to a subset of the set of all subsets of natural numbers and hence it has cardinality $\leqq \mathfrak{c}$. The system of closed sets is put into correspondence with the open sets in one-to-one fashion by the formation of complements, and therefore it likewise has cardinality $\leqq \mathfrak{c}$.

A topological space, in which there exists a denumerable dense set, is sometimes called *separable*. For example, the Euclidean space R^n and its subsets are separable. Theorem 10.7 asserts that for metric spaces the concepts of separability and of having denumerable weight coincide.

§ 11. Coarser and Finer Topologies

11.1 Definition: Let two topologies $\mathfrak{T}$ and $\mathfrak{T}'$ with the systems $\mathfrak{O}$ and $\mathfrak{O}'$ of open sets be given for a set $\mathfrak{X}$. $\mathfrak{T}$ is said to be *finer* than $\mathfrak{T}'$, and $\mathfrak{T}'$ is said to be *coarser* than $\mathfrak{T}$, if $\mathfrak{O} \supset \mathfrak{O}'$.

In general, of two topologies $\mathfrak{T}$ and $\mathfrak{T}'$ for $\mathfrak{X}$, one will not be finer than the other; $\mathfrak{O}$ and $\mathfrak{O}'$ may overlap in an arbitrary fashion. It is noted that $\mathfrak{T}$ is said to be finer than $\mathfrak{T}'$ also in the case $\mathfrak{T} = \mathfrak{T}'$. An example is yielded by the two topologies in § 1, examples (c) and (c′). The topology of (c) is coarser than that of (c′), and indeed they are not equal as one can easily verify. In contrast, the topologies of examples (a), (a′) and (a″) are the same; they are only generated by different metrics. The metrics $d(x, y)$, $d'(x, y)$ and $d''(x, y)$ are topologically equivalent in these three cases (see Definition 2.3).

There is a finest topology for a set $\mathfrak{X}$ which is finer than all the remaining topologies for $\mathfrak{X}$; it is obviously the discrete topology, which we have considered immediately after Definition 2.3. In this topology, $\mathfrak{O}$ consists of the set of all subsets of $\mathfrak{X}$; all subsets of $\mathfrak{X}$ are open and all of them are closed. $\mathfrak{U}(p)$ consists all the sets which contain p. For every subset $A \subset \mathfrak{X}$ we have that $\underline{A} = \bar{A} = A$. Furthermore, there exists a coarsest topology for $\mathfrak{X}$. In this topology, $\mathfrak{O}$ consists of $\emptyset$ and $\mathfrak{X}$ only, and these are also the only closed sets. Every point has only $\mathfrak{X}$ as a neighborhood, and for arbitrary $A \neq \emptyset, \neq \mathfrak{X}$, we have that $\underline{A} = \emptyset$, $\bar{A} = \mathfrak{X}$.

11.2 Theorem: *Let $\mathfrak{T}$ and $\mathfrak{T}'$ be two topologies for the same set $\mathfrak{X}$. Then $\mathfrak{T}$ is finer than $\mathfrak{T}'$ if, and only if, any one of the following equivalent conditions is satisfied:*

(1) *For the systems of open sets in $\mathfrak{T}$ and $\mathfrak{T}'$, we have that $\mathfrak{O} \supset \mathfrak{O}'$ holds.*

(1′) *For the systems of closed sets in $\mathfrak{T}$ and $\mathfrak{T}'$, we have that $\mathfrak{A} \supset \mathfrak{A}'$ holds, where $\mathfrak{A}$, $\mathfrak{A}'$ are the systems of closed sets for $\mathfrak{T}$, $\mathfrak{T}'$, respectively.*

(2) *For the neighborhood systems in $\mathfrak{T}$ and $\mathfrak{T}'$, we have that $\mathfrak{U}(p) \supset \mathfrak{U}'(p)$ holds for every $p \in \mathfrak{X}$.*

(3) *The interior in $\mathfrak{T}$ of a set A contains the interior in $\mathfrak{T}'$ of A.*

(3′) *The closure in $\mathfrak{T}$ of a set A is contained in the closure in $\mathfrak{T}'$ of A.*

The proof follows from the theorems of §§ 2, 3, which give a dual characterization of the fundamental concepts "open," "closed," "neighborhood," and so forth. Thus, say, the interior of A is the largest open subset of A; since $\mathfrak{O}$ contains more open sets than $\mathfrak{O}'$, the interior in $\mathfrak{T}$ of A is more comprehensive than the interior in $\mathfrak{T}'$.

11.3 Theorem: *If the systems* $\mathfrak{B}$ *and* $\mathfrak{B}'$ *are bases of the topologies* $\mathfrak{T}$ *and* $\mathfrak{T}'$ *for the same set* $\mathfrak{X}$, *then* $\mathfrak{T}$ *is finer than* $\mathfrak{T}'$ *if, and only if, for each set* $B'_\mu \in \mathfrak{B}'$ *and each* $p \in B'_\mu$ *there exists a* $B_\lambda \in \mathfrak{B}$ *such that* $p \in B_\lambda \subset B'_\mu$.

Proof: If $\mathfrak{T}$ is finer than $\mathfrak{T}'$, then B'_μ is the union of sets B_λ, and at least one of these sets B_λ must contain p, $p \in B_\lambda \subset B'_\mu$.

Conversely, if the condition of the theorem is satisfied, then each set B'_μ is the union of sets B_λ: Namely, if $p \in B'_\mu$, then there is a $B_\lambda = B_\lambda(p)$ such that $p \in B_\lambda(p) \subset B'_\mu$. Obviously, $B'_\mu = \bigcup B_\lambda(p)$, taken over all $p \in B'_\mu$.

Now, let one further, not necessarily topologized, set $\mathfrak{X}$ be given. In § 10, we asked which systems of subsets of $\mathfrak{X}$ are suitable for bases for a topology $\mathfrak{T}$ for $\mathfrak{X}$. We generalize this formulation of the question: Let $\mathfrak{C} = \{C_\lambda \mid \lambda \text{ from an arbitrary index set } \Lambda\}$ be an arbitrary given system of subsets of $\mathfrak{X}$. Does there exist a topology $\mathfrak{T}$ for $\mathfrak{X}$ for which the C_λ are open sets? Surely this is the case for the discrete topology on $\mathfrak{X}$. Now, let $\mathfrak{T}$ be any topology for which the C_λ are open sets and let $\mathfrak{O}$ be the system of all open sets in $\mathfrak{T}$. Then, according to [O 2], all finite intersections of sets C_λ are also open in $\mathfrak{T}$. Let $\mathfrak{B} = \{B_\mu \mid \mu \text{ from an arbitrary index set } M\}$ be the system of these finite intersections; we include $\mathfrak{X}$ among these intersections (see Index under "intersection"). We have that $\mathfrak{B} \subset \mathfrak{O}$. Further, according to [O 1], arbitrary unions of sets B_μ are open in $\mathfrak{T}$; let $\mathfrak{O}_0$ be the system of these unions, we include $\emptyset$ in $\mathfrak{O}_0$. Therefore we have that $\mathfrak{O}_0 \subset \mathfrak{O}$. We now assert that the system $\mathfrak{O}_0$ already satisfies axioms [O 1] and [O 2]. [O 1] is immediate as a consequence of the general associative law for the formation of unions, and [O 2] follows similarly from the distributive law for intersections and unions (fundamental formula (2)). Thus, $\mathfrak{O}_0$ determines a topology $\mathfrak{T}_0$ for $\mathfrak{X}$ and indeed a coarser topology than $\mathfrak{T}$. We summarize this result in the next theorem.

11.4 Theorem: *Let* $\mathfrak{C} = \{C_\lambda \mid \lambda \text{ from an arbitrary index set } \Lambda\}$ *be a system of subsets of a set* $\mathfrak{X}$. *There exists a uniquely determined coarsest topology* $\mathfrak{T}_0$ *for* $\mathfrak{X}$ *in which the* C_λ *are open sets.* $\mathfrak{C}$ *is called a generating system or a subbasis for* $\mathfrak{T}_0$.

The possibility of generating topologies in a set $\mathfrak{X}$, given by means of this theorem, is especially useful in the construction of examples and other special topologies.

§ 12. Product Topology and Quotient Topology

We precede our discussion with some set-theoretical considerations. Let X_1, X_2 be two sets; the set $\mathfrak{X} = X_1 \times X_2$ of all pairs $x =$

$x_1 \times x_2$ with $x_1 \in X_1$ and $x_2 \in X_2$ is called the *product set* of X_1 and X_2 and X_1, X_2 are called the *factor sets* of $\mathfrak{X}$. x_1 and x_2 are called the *coordinates* of the element $x = x_1 \times x_2$. The mapping $\varphi_i: \mathfrak{X} \to X_i$ ($i = 1, 2$) with $\varphi_i(x) = x_i$ is called the *projection mapping*, or briefly the *projection*, of $\mathfrak{X}$ onto X_i. The coordinate x_i is also called the *projection* of x in X_i. If $A_i \subset X_i$ for $i = 1, 2$, then the subset of $\mathfrak{X}$ consisting of all $y_1 \times y_2$ with $y_i \in A_i$ is called the product set $A_1 \times A_2$ of A_1 and A_2. The (untopologized) plane R^2, for instance, is an example, being the product of two (untopologized) lines R^1. If A is a subset of $\mathfrak{X}$, then $\varphi_i(A)$, the projection of A onto X_i, denotes the set of all $\varphi_i(y)$ with $y \in A$. The following rules are valid:

$$\varphi_i(A \cup B) = \varphi_i(A) \cup \varphi_i(B), \varphi_i(A \cap B) \subset \varphi_i(A) \cap \varphi_i(B).$$

That the equality sign does not hold generally in the above inclusion is shown, say, by the example of two lines A, B in the Euclidean plane $R^2 = R^1 \times R^1$ which are parallel to the x-axis and their projections on the x-axis.

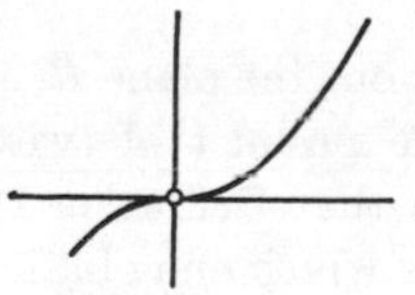

Fig. 3

If $f: X_1 \to X_2$ is a mapping of X_1 into X_2, then the subset

$$[f] = \{x = x_1 \times x_2 \mid x_2 = f(x_1)\}$$

in $\mathfrak{X} = X_1 \times X_2$ is called the *graph* of f. Conversely, $[f]$ completely determines f. The frequent use outside of topology (even outside of mathematics) of the graph $[f]$ to depict the function f, is well known.

If X_1, X_2 and $\mathfrak{Y}$ are three sets, then a rule which assigns to each pair $x_1 \in X_1$, $x_2 \in X_2$ one and only one element $f(x_1, x_2) \in \mathfrak{Y}$ is called a *function f of two variables* x_1, x_2. One interprets f expediently as the ordinary function $f\colon (X_1 \times X_2) \to \mathfrak{Y}$. The case $X_1 = X_2 = \mathfrak{X}$ occurs especially often, in which case $f\colon (\mathfrak{X} \times \mathfrak{X}) \to \mathfrak{Y}$.

Now let X_i $(i = 1, 2)$ be two topological spaces with the topologies $\mathfrak{T}_i$ and the systems of open sets $\mathfrak{O}_i$. In order to equip the product set $\mathfrak{X} = X_1 \times X_2$ with a topology, we consider the system $\mathfrak{B}$ of all products $O_1 \times O_2$ of open sets O_1 in $\mathfrak{X}_1$ with open sets O_2 in X_2. $\mathfrak{B}$ can serve as a basis of a topology $\mathfrak{T}$ in $\mathfrak{X}$. Namely, if $O_1 \times O_2$ and $O_1' \times O_2'$ are two sets in $\mathfrak{B}$, then the intersection

$$(O_1 \times O_2) \cap (O_1' \times O_2') = (O_1 \cap O_1') \times (O_2 \cap O_2')$$

is also a set from $\mathfrak{B}$; the criterion of Theorem 10.5 is therefore trivially satisfied for a basis.

12.1 Definition: If $\mathfrak{T}_i$ $(i = 1, 2)$ are topologies for the sets X_i, then the topology $\mathfrak{T}$ defined in the product set $\mathfrak{X} = X_1 \times X_2$, which has as basis the products of the open sets of X_1 and X_2, is called the *product topology* $\mathfrak{T} = \mathfrak{T}_1 \times \mathfrak{T}_2$ over $\mathfrak{X}$. $\mathfrak{X} = X_1 \times X_2$, equipped with this topology $\mathfrak{T}$, is called the *product*, or the *topological product*, of X_1 and X_2.

As examples, we point out the plane R^2 as the product of two lines R^1 and the torus as the product of two circumferences. One can easily clarify for himself that Definition 12.1 applies in these cases.

Of the many theorems which one obtains upon comparison of the topologies $\mathfrak{T}_i$ of the factors X_i with the topology $\mathfrak{T}$ of $\mathfrak{X}$, we mention here only the following facts: The projection mappings φ_i $(i = 1, 2)$ are continuous. If A is an open set in $\mathfrak{X}$, then $\varphi_i(A)$ is also open in $\mathfrak{X}$ and thus also open in X_i. This follows from the fact that it is valid for the open sets of a basis $\mathfrak{B}$ of the sort indicated above, and it carries over to the general case by means of [O 1]. One must note, however, that the projection $\varphi_i(A)$ of a closed set $A \subset \mathfrak{X}$ is in general not closed; the example of the closed set A consisting of the branch of the hyperbola $y = x^{-1}$ in the first quadrant of the (x, y)-plane R^2 whose projection on the x-axis is the open interval $(0, +\infty)$ shows this. A function $f = f(x_1, x_2)$ in two variables, $f\colon X_1 \times X_2 \to \mathfrak{Y}$, is continuous at (p_1, p_2) if, and only if, to each neighborhood $U \in \mathfrak{U}(f(p_1, p_2))$ in

$\mathfrak{Y}$ there exist neighborhoods $U_1 \in \mathfrak{U}(p_1)$ in X_1, $U_2 \in \mathfrak{U}(p_2)$ in X_2 such that $f(U_1, U_2) \subset U$, i.e. $f(x_1, x_2) \in U$, if $x_1 \in U_1$, $x_2 \in U_2$.

There are no difficulties to extend the considerations of this section and the Definition 12.1 to any finite number of factors X_i $(i = 1, \ldots, n)$ and to interpret the product

$$\mathfrak{X} = \prod_{i=1}^{n} X_i.$$

In the definition of the product ΠX_λ with an arbitrary number—even an infinite number—of factor spaces X_λ (λ from a suitable index set Λ), one proceeds, however, because of necessity, somewhat differently: The product set $\mathfrak{X} = \Pi X_\lambda$ and the projection mappings $\varphi_\lambda: \mathfrak{X} \to X_\lambda$ are defined analogously to the way this is done in the finite case. Now we consider for each open set O_λ of X_λ the "strip" $\varphi_\lambda^{-1}(O_\lambda)$ in $\mathfrak{X}$, i.e. the set of all points of $\mathfrak{X}$ whose projection φ_λ falls on O_λ. From the set of all strips, we form the set $\mathfrak{B}$ of all finite intersections of strips. This set satisfies the conditions of Theorem 10.5 since the intersection of two such finite intersections is again one of the same sort. Thus, $\mathfrak{B}$ is a basis of a topology $\mathfrak{T}$ for $\mathfrak{X}$. $\mathfrak{X} = \Pi X_\lambda$ is called the *product space* of the X_λ and $\mathfrak{T}$ is called the *product topology* of the topologies $\mathfrak{T}_\lambda$ of the X_λ.

The basis for this sort of definition of the product topology $\mathfrak{T}$ lies in the following fact. We seek a topology over the product set $\mathfrak{X} = \Pi X_\lambda$, which in any case has the property that the projection mappings φ_λ are continuous functions. We easily recognize that the discrete topology of $\mathfrak{X}$ has this property; if a topology $\mathfrak{T}'$ for $\mathfrak{X}$ has this property, then every finer topology for $\mathfrak{X}$ also has this property. The product topology just defined is now the coarsest topology for $\mathfrak{X}$ which has the named property, as one can easily verify.

As an example, we consider for each $i = 1, 2, \ldots$ a copy of the closed unit segment $I_i^1 = \{t : 0 \leq t \leq 1\}$. The product of the I_i^1 is the infinite-dimensional unit cube I^∞ whose points are described by the infinite sequences $t = (t_1, t_2, \ldots)$ of real numbers with $0 \leqq t_i \leqq 1$; the topology of I^∞ is the product topology given above. One can depict it by mapping I^∞ onto the Hilbert cube $\mathfrak{P}$ (example (b) of § 1), and indeed by means of the mapping $x = f(t)$, which is given by means of $x_i = \left(\frac{1}{2^i}\right) t_i$ $(i = 1, 2, \ldots)$. f is a monomorphic and epimorphic mapping of I^∞ onto $\mathfrak{P}$, and it is not very difficult to verify that f as well as f^{-1} is continuous. I^∞ and $\mathfrak{P}$ are therefore homeomorphic. The topology of $\mathfrak{P}$ appears in I^∞ in an especially intuitive form which is symmetric in all coordinates.

We shall now go briefly into the quotient topology. First of all, let a partition of an arbitrary set $\mathfrak{X}$ into non-empty subsets P_λ (λ from a suitable index set Λ, $P_\lambda \cap P_{\lambda'} = \emptyset$ if $\lambda' \neq \lambda$) be given. Such a partition is produced by means of an equivalence relation among the points of $\mathfrak{X}$. We think of the P_λ as the elements p'_λ of a new set $\mathfrak{X}'$. If $p \in \mathfrak{X}$, and indeed $p \in P_\lambda$, then we set $\varphi(p) = p'_\lambda$; therefore, φ denotes the natural mapping of $\mathfrak{X}$ onto $\mathfrak{X}'$, which assigns to each element p of $\mathfrak{X}$ the set P_λ containing it or its representative p'_λ in $\mathfrak{X}'$.

Now if a topology $\mathfrak{T}$ is given for $\mathfrak{X}$, then we can obtain from it a topology $\mathfrak{T}'$ for $\mathfrak{X}'$ in the following way. We define a subset $O' \subset \mathfrak{X}'$ to be open if $\varphi^{-1}(O')$ is open in $\mathfrak{X}$, i.e. if the totality of all $p \in \mathfrak{X}$ with $\varphi(p) \in O'$ is open in $\mathfrak{X}$. We recognize immediately the validity of the axioms [O 1], [O 2] for these open sets of $\mathfrak{X}'$; they follow immediately from [O 1], [O 2] in $\mathfrak{X}$. The topology $\mathfrak{T}'$ arising thus is called the *quotient topology* $\mathfrak{T}'$ of the topology $\mathfrak{T}$ with respect to the given partition of $\mathfrak{X}$; $\mathfrak{X}'$ is called the *quotient space*.

As an example, let us consider on the real line $\mathfrak{X} = R^1$ the equivalence relation $x \equiv x' \pmod 1$ and the partition of $\mathfrak{X}$ resulting from it. The quotient space $\mathfrak{X}'$ is the closed circumference of a circle. Analogously, one can obtain the torus from the real plane R^2 as the quotient space with respect to the partition of R^2 into equivalent points relative to a periodic lattice.

Part II

SPECIAL CLASSES OF SPACES

Chapter 4

SPACES DEFINED BY SEPARATION AXIOMS

§ 13. Hausdorff Spaces

The spaces considered up to this point are still so general that they bear many characteristics which deviate strongly from the usual idea of a space. This is illustrated, for example, by the coarsest topology for a set $\mathfrak{X}$ and also by the following example. Let R^2 be the set of all pairs (x, y) of real numbers. A "strip neighborhood" of (x_0, y_0) is given by all (x, y) with $| x - x_0 | < \varepsilon$ where $\varepsilon > 0$, and general neighborhoods are all sets that contain strip neighborhoods. The neighborhood axioms are satisfied; therefore, we have here a topological space. In every neighborhood of (x_0, y_0) there lie all points $(x_0, y_0 + c)$ with arbitrary real c of the perpendicular through (x_0, y_0). Actually, this perpendicular is the closure of the point set consisting of the single point (x_0, y_0). The point set consisting of (x_0, y_0) is not closed.

We shall now subject our spaces to a series of stronger and stronger restricting axioms, whereby the point sets, such as those introduced above, will be closed. The spaces so defined are more special than those treated up to this point, and hence they possess a more developed structure which is indicated by the theorems which are added to the previous theory.

We shall first of all exclude by means of an axiom the situation that the intersection of all the closed neighborhoods of a point p contains points other than p.

13.1 Definition: A topological space $\mathfrak{X}$ is called a *Hausdorff space* and its topology $\mathfrak{T}$ is called *Hausdorff* if either one of the following two equivalent axioms is satisfied:

[*Hd*] *If* p, q $(p \neq q)$ *are any two points of* $\mathfrak{X}$, *then there exist neighborhoods* $U \in \mathfrak{U}(p)$ *and* $V \in \mathfrak{U}(q)$ *such that* $U \cap V = \emptyset$ (Hausdorff's separation axiom).

[*Hd'*] *The intersection of all closed neighborhoods of a point* p *contains* p *only.*

[*Hd*] is called a separation axiom because it separates the two points p and q by means of the neighborhoods U and V; it is named after F. Hausdorff who was the first to recognize its significance.

Furthermore, in [*Hd*] one can take U and V to be open without modifying its content.

In the sequel, we shall deal almost exclusively with Hausdorff spaces.

Proof of the equivalence [*Hd*] $\Leftrightarrow$ [*Hd'*]: We first prove that [*Hd*] $\Rightarrow$ [*Hd'*]. Let [*Hd*] be satisfied and suppose p is a fixed point in $\mathfrak{X}$. Let x range over all points $\neq p$ in $\mathfrak{X}$. According to [*Hd*], there exist neighborhoods $U_x \in \mathfrak{U}(p)$ and $V_x \in \mathfrak{U}(x)$, which we take to be open, with $U_x \cap V_x = \emptyset$. $\complement V_x$ is a closed neighborhood of p which does not contain x. This proves that [*Hd*] $\Rightarrow$ [*Hd'*].

We shall now prove that [*Hd'*] $\Rightarrow$ [*Hd*]. If $p \neq q$, then there exists a closed neighborhood $U \in \mathfrak{U}(p)$ which does not contain q. Then $\complement U$ is open and it is a neighborhood of q since $q \in \complement U$; we always have that $U \cap \complement U = \emptyset$, which is what we had to prove.

13.2 Theorem: *Every subspace of a Hausdorff space is Hausdorff.*

The proof follows directly from [*Hd*] and Theorem 6.4.

13.3 Theorem: *In a Hausdorff space, every set consisting of only one point is closed.*

The proof follows from [*Hd'*] and axiom [*A* 1] (see § 3).

13.4 Theorem: *Every topology for a set* $\mathfrak{X}$ *which is finer than a Hausdorff topology for* $\mathfrak{X}$ *is itself Hausdorff.*

The proof follows quite easily from [*Hd*] and Theorem 11.2, (2).

13.5 Theorem: *The product $\mathfrak{X} = \Pi X_\lambda$ of an arbitrary set of topological spaces $X_\lambda \neq \emptyset$ is Hausdorff if, and only if, all the factors are Hausdorff.*

Proof: Suppose all the X_λ are Hausdorff and let $p, q \in \mathfrak{X}, p \neq q$. Then the projections $\varphi_\lambda(p) = p_\lambda, \varphi_\lambda(q) = q_\lambda$ of p, q along X_λ are distinct for at least one index λ. Since X_λ is Hausdorff, there are neighborhoods $U_\lambda \in \mathfrak{U}(p_\lambda)$, $V_\lambda \in \mathfrak{U}(q_\lambda)$ with $U_\lambda \cap V_\lambda = \emptyset$ in $\mathfrak{X}$. Then $\varphi_\lambda^{-1}(U_\lambda)$ and $\varphi_\lambda{}^{-1}(V_\lambda)$ are separating neighborhoods for p and q.

Conversely, let $\mathfrak{X}$ be Hausdorff. Let X_λ be a fixed factor of $\mathfrak{X}$. Those points of $\mathfrak{X}$ whose λ-th coordinate ranges over X_λ, whose remaining coordinates, however, are chosen fixed in an arbitrary manner, obviously form a subspace of $\mathfrak{X}$ which is homeomorphic to X_λ. According to Theorem 13.2, this subspace is Hausdorff and therefore X_λ is also Hausdorff.

13.6 Definition: The point p of a Hausdorff space $\mathfrak{X}$ is called a *limit* of the point sequence $x_1, x_2 \ldots$, in symbols,

$$p = \lim_{n \to \infty} x_n,$$

if for each neighborhood $U \in \mathfrak{U}(p)$ there exists an $n_0 = n_0(U)$ such that $x_n \in U$ for $n > n_0$. If the sequence possesses a limit, we say that the sequence is *convergent* in $\mathfrak{X}$.

Note that the points of a sequence need not all be distinct. For example, the terms of a sequence can be constant ($= p$) from some index n on; then surely the sequence has p as a limit.

Obviously a sequence need not have a limit.

A subsequence of a convergent sequence is also convergent and it has the same limit.

13.7 Theorem: *A sequence in a Hausdorff space has at most one limit.*

Proof: If p is a limit of the sequence $x_1, x_2, \ldots$ and $q \neq p$, then there are neighborhoods $U \in \mathfrak{U}(p)$ and $V \in \mathfrak{U}(q)$ with $U \cap V = \emptyset$. For all $n > n_0$, we have $x_n \in U$ and therefore $x_n \notin V$; hence q cannot be a limit of the sequence.

13.8 Theorem: *If $f\colon \mathfrak{X} \to \mathfrak{Y}$ is a continuous mapping at p, then the following assertion is valid:*

$$\lim_{n\to\infty} x_n = p \text{ implies } \lim_{n\to\infty} f(x_n) = f(p).$$

Proof: Let $V \in \mathfrak{U}(f(p))$. $U = f^{-1}(V)$ is a neighborhood of p because f is continuous at p. Therefore, there exists an n_0, which depends on U, such that $x_n \in U$ provided $n > n_0$. It follows that $f(x_n) \in V$ for these n; this completes the proof of the above limit equation.

13.9 Definition: If A is a subset of $\mathfrak{X}$, then $p \in \mathfrak{X}$ is called a *sequential limit point* of A provided p is the limit of a sequence of points in A.

According to this, a sequential limit point of A is surely a contact point of A. The converse assertion is not valid in general. We shall show this using the function space which we introduced as an example immediately before Definition 2.4. Let A be the subset of $\mathfrak{X}$ which consists of the functions f having the value 1 almost everywhere and the value 0—rather than 1—only in a finite number of places. Suppose f_0 has everywhere the value 0. Evidently, f_0 is a contact point of A, but we assert that it is not a sequential limit point of A. Namely, if $f_1, f_2, \ldots$ is any sequence from A with the limit f^*, then f^* can be 0 at most at the places at which one of the functions $f_1, f_2, \ldots$ is 0, and this means finitely many for each of these functions, and therefore altogether at most denumerably many. At all other places, f^* has the value 1; hence we have that $f^* \neq f_0$. If we wish to take into consideration the contact points as well as the sequential limit points of a set, then we must introduce so-called "filters," which, however, lie outside the scope of our presentation. (See N. Bourbaki [1] or H. J. Kowalsky [2].)

In a Hausdorff space, one can say still more about the accumulation points p of a set A over and above Definition 3.11. Namely, if U_1 is a neighborhood of p, then there is still a point $x_1 \neq p$ in A which according to our definition lies in U_1. If U_2 is a neighborhood of p which does not contain x_1 (the existence of such a neighborhood is guaranteed by [Hd]), then there is a corresponding $x_2 \neq p$, $x_2 \neq x_1$ in $U_1 \cap U_2$. Proceeding in this way, we obtain in U_1 a sequence x_1,

$x_2, \ldots$ of distinct points of A. We can therefore state the following theorem.

13.10 Theorem: *In a Hausdorff space, every neighborhood of an accumulation point p of a set A contains an infinite number of points of A.*

§ 14. Regular Spaces

14.1 Definition: A topological space $\mathfrak{X}$ and its topology are called *regular* if $\mathfrak{X}$ is Hausdorff and any one of the following three equivalent conditions is satisfied:

[*Rg*] For every closed set $A \subset \mathfrak{X}$ and each point $p \notin A$ there exist neighborhoods U of A and V of p such that $U \cap V = \emptyset$.

[*Rg'*] Every neighborhood of a point p contains a closed neighborhood of p; in other words, the closed neighborhoods of p form a neighborhood basis of p.

[*Rg''*] Every neighborhood U of a point p contains an open neighborhood W of p such that $\overline{W} \subset U$.

Proof of the equivalence:

[*Rg'*] $\Rightarrow$ [*Rg''*]. According to [*Rg'*], the neighborhood U of p contains the closed neighborhood V of p. By Theorem 3.4, V contains an open neighborhood W of p. Then $W \subset V = \overline{V} \subset U$ and therefore $\overline{W} \subset U$, which is what we were required to prove.

[*Rg''*] $\Rightarrow$ [*Rg*]. If A is closed and $p \notin A$, then $\complement A$ is open and hence it is a neighborhood of p. According to [*Rg''*], there exists an open neighborhood W of p such that $\overline{W} \subset \complement A$. $\complement \overline{W}$ is open and $\complement \overline{W} \supset A$; $\complement \overline{W}$ is therefore a neighborhood of A. [*Rg*] is then satisfied with $U = \complement \overline{W}$ and $V = W$.

[*Rg*] $\Rightarrow$ [*Rg'*]. It suffices to prove [*Rg'*] for an open neighborhood W of p. Then $\complement W$ is closed and, according to [*Rg*], there exist neighborhoods U of $\complement W$ and V of p such that $U \cap V = \emptyset$; U and V can be taken to be open. We have $V \subset \complement U$ and therefore $\overline{V} \subset \overline{\complement U} = \complement \underline{U} = \complement U$. Since $U \supset \complement W$, therefore $\complement U \subset W$ and it follows that $\overline{V} \subset W$; this completes the proof of [*Rg'*].

14.2 Theorem: *Every subspace $\mathfrak{Y}$ of a regular space $\mathfrak{X}$ is regular.*

Proof: First, $\mathfrak{Y}$ is Hausdorff according to Theorem 13.2. We shall prove that $\mathfrak{Y}$ satisfies the axiom [Rg']. If U is a $\mathfrak{Y}$-neighborhood (cf. § 6) of a point $p \in \mathfrak{Y}$, then U is the trace $U = V_{\mathfrak{Y}} = V \cap \mathfrak{Y}$ of an $\mathfrak{X}$-neighborhood V of p (cf. Theorem 6.4). V contains a closed $\mathfrak{X}$-neighborhood V_0 of p. $(V_0)_{\mathfrak{Y}} = V_0 \cap \mathfrak{Y}$ is then a closed $\mathfrak{Y}$-neighborhood of p contained in U.

We shall now give an example of a space which is Hausdorff but not regular, but we shall however leave the verification of these properties to the reader. Let R be the real line. Let a subbasis in the sense of Theorem 11.4 for a topology for R consist of all open intervals in R in the usual sense and of the set of those rational numbers which have a power of 2 in the denominator (i.e. the dyadic fractions).

§ 15. Normal Spaces

15.1 Definition: A topological space $\mathfrak{X}$ and its topology are said to be *normal* if $\mathfrak{X}$ is Hausdorff and any one of the following equivalent conditions is satisfied:

[Nm] For any two closed disjoint sets $A, B \subset \mathfrak{X}$ there exist neighborhoods U of A and V of B such that $U \cap V = \emptyset$.

[Nm'] Every neighborhood of a closed set A contains a closed neighborhood of A.

[Nm''] Every neighborhood U of a closed set A contains an open neighborhood V of A such that $\overline{V} \subset U$.

The equivalence of these three conditions follows *verbatim* as in the preceding sections for the equivalence of the regularity conditions if one replaces there the point p by the set B.

Since a one-point set is closed in a Hausdorff space (see Theorem 13.3), normal spaces are special cases of regular spaces (i.e. every normal space is regular).

An example of a regular but not normal space is the following: let $\mathfrak{X}$ be the upper half-plane $y \geqq 0$ of the Euclidean (x, y)-plane. Neighborhoods of points with $y > 0$ are defined as usual; neighborhoods of the points $(x, 0)$ are formed by the open circular discs which are tangent to the x-axis at $(x, 0)$ and including the point $(x, 0)$ itself. We leave to the reader to prove the regularity of $\mathfrak{X}$ and to show that the closed set $A = \{(x, 0) \mid x \text{ is rational}\}$ and the closed set $B = \{(x, 0) \mid x \text{ is irrational}\}$ do not satisfy the axiom [Nm].

There is no analogue to Theorem 14.2 for normal spaces. If one attempts to carry over the proof of Theorem 14.2 to normal spaces, one founders because of the fact that a $\mathfrak{Y}$-closed set is not necessarily $\mathfrak{X}$-closed.

The following two theorems due to P. Urysohn bring the normal space $\mathfrak{X}$ into an important and consequential relationship with the real-valued functions on $\mathfrak{X}$.

15.2 Theorem: *A Hausdorff space $\mathfrak{X}$ is normal if, and only if, the following Urysohn axiom is valid in it:*

[U] If A and B are any two disjoint closed sets in $\mathfrak{X}$, then there exists a continuous real-valued function $f(x)$ on $\mathfrak{X}$, $0 \leqq f(x) \leqq 1$, such that $f(x) = 0$ on A and $f(x) = 1$ on B.

Proof: First, let $\mathfrak{X}$ be a Hausdorff space in which [U] holds; we shall prove that [Nm] is then valid. We consider the sets

$$U = \{x \mid f(x) < \tfrac{1}{2}\},\ V = \{x \mid f(x) > \tfrac{1}{2}\}.$$

U is open. Namely, if $x_0 \in U$ so that $f(x_0) < \frac{1}{2}$, then, since f is continuous, a neighborhood W of x_0 can be found so that $|f(x) - f(x_0)| < \varepsilon$, where $\varepsilon = 2^{-\mu}$ for large μ, for all $x \in W$. For sufficiently small choice of ε then also $f(x) < \frac{1}{2}$, i.e. x belongs to U. Likewise, V is open. Since $A \subset U$, $B \subset V$, $U \cap V = \emptyset$, [Nm] is valid.

Now, conversely, let $\mathfrak{X}$ be a normal space and suppose A, B are two disjoint closed subsets of $\mathfrak{X}$. $\complement A$ is an open neighborhood of B; we set $\complement A = U_0$. According to [Nm''], we then choose U_1 as an open neighborhood of B so that $U_0 \supset \bar{U}_1$.

Continuing inductively, we assume that for all integers $0, 1, \ldots, n$ open sets

$$U_{\frac{\nu}{2^n}} \text{ with } \nu = 1, \ldots, 2^n \text{ and } U_{\frac{\nu-1}{2^n}} \supset \bar{U}_{\frac{\nu}{2^n}}$$

have already been constructed as they were just constructed for $n = 0$. We choose in accordance with [Nm''] an open neighborhood $U_{\frac{2\nu-1}{2^{n+1}}}$ with $\nu = 1, \ldots, 2^n$ of $U_{\frac{\nu}{2^n}}$ so that $U_{\frac{\nu-1}{2^n}} \supset \bar{U}_{\frac{2\nu-1}{2^{n+1}}}$. Thus, we proceed from n to $n + 1$. Continuing further, we obtain for all dyadic fractions r with $0 \leqq r \leqq 1$ open neighborhoods U_r of B with

$$U_r \supset \bar{U}_{r'} \text{ if } r < r'.$$

For an arbitrary real number α between 0 and 1, we set $U_\alpha = \bigcup U_r$ taken over all $r \geqq \alpha$. If $\alpha < \alpha'$, then there exist dyadic fractions r, r', with $\alpha < r < r' < \alpha'$, and for these r, r' we have that $U_\alpha \supset U_r$, $U_{r'} \supset U_{\alpha'}$, from which it follows, inasmuch as $U_r \supset \bar{U}_{r'}$, that $U_\alpha \supset \bar{U}_{\alpha'}$. Further, if we set $U_\alpha = \mathfrak{X}$ for $\alpha < 0$ and $U_\alpha = \varnothing$ for $\alpha > 1$, then

$$U_\alpha \supset \bar{U}_{\alpha'} \text{ if } \alpha < \alpha'$$

holds for all real α. The set of those α for which a given point $x \in \mathfrak{X}$ lies in U_α is obviously a left half-line on the real axis which is determined by a real number $f(x)$. We assert that this function $f(x)$ satisfies the Urysohn axiom [U]. Certainly we have $f(x) = 0$ for $x \in A$ and $f(x) = 1$ for $x \in B$. The continuity of $f(x)$ is directly evident: In order to obtain $|f(q) - f(p)| \leqq \varepsilon$, where $\varepsilon = 2^{-\mu}$ for large μ, one has only to choose q in the set $U_{f(p)-\varepsilon} - \bar{U}_{f(p)+\varepsilon}$, which is an open set (by Theorem 3.7) and hence is a neighborhood of p. This completes the proof of Theorem 15.2.

15.3 Theorem: (Supplement to Urysohn's Theorem 15.2): *Let the open set O of the normal space $\mathfrak{X}$ be the union of denumerably many closed sets. Then there exists a continuous real-valued function $f(x)$ on $\mathfrak{X}$, $0 \leqq f(x) \leqq 1$, which is greater than 0 for precisely the points of O.*

Proof: Let $O = \bigcup B_n$ for $n = 1, 2, \ldots$. We set $B_1 = B$, $\complement O = A$ and then apply the line of reasoning of the preceding proof in a somewhat modified form: U_0, U_1, $U_{\frac{1}{2}}$, $U_{\frac{3}{4}}$ have the above meaning. $U_{\frac{1}{4}}$ is however chosen as an open neighborhood of the closed set $\overline{U}_{\frac{1}{2}} \cup B_2$ and furthermore again so that $\overline{U}_{\frac{1}{4}}$ is contained in U_0. Accordingly, suppose $U_{\frac{\nu}{2^n}}$ with $\nu = 1, \ldots, 2^n$ and $U_{\frac{\nu-1}{2^n}} \supset \overline{U}_{\frac{\nu}{2^n}}$ and $U_{\frac{1}{2^n}} \supset \bigcup_{m=1}^{n} B_m$ have already been constructed. Then the determination of the $U_{\frac{2\nu-1}{2^{n+1}}}$ remains the same up to $U_{\frac{1}{2^{n+1}}}$: This set is chosen as an open neighborhood of $\overline{U}_{\frac{1}{2^n}} \cup B_{n+1}$ whose closure is contained in U_0; otherwise, we proceed as above. Then we obtain for every real α an open set U_α with

$$U_\alpha \supset \overline{U}_{\alpha'} \text{ if } \alpha < \alpha';\; U_\alpha \supset \bigcup_{m=1}^{n} B_m \text{ if } \alpha = \frac{1}{2^n}.$$

The definition of $f(p)$ is as above; the proof of continuity also remains the same. Now, if $p \in O$, then $p \in B_n \subset U_{\frac{1}{2^n}}$ for suitable n. It follows that $f(p) \geqq \frac{1}{2^n}$ and therefore $f(p) > 0$; this completes the proof of the theorem.

Chapter 5

SPACES DEFINED BY COVERING PROPERTIES: COMPACT SPACES

§ 16. Compactness

The compact spaces which we shall treat now are especially important and are distinguished by many geometric properties. They are defined by means of the covering properties which present essentially sharper restrictions than the separation axioms. By a *covering* of a space $\mathfrak{X}$ one understands a system $\mathfrak{D} = \{D_\lambda \mid \lambda \in \Lambda\}$ of subsets $D_\lambda \subset \mathfrak{X}$ with indices λ from an arbitrary index set Λ, for which $\bigcup D_\lambda = \mathfrak{X}$; hence, every point is "covered" by at least one of the sets D_λ. $\mathfrak{D}$ is called finite or infinite depending on whether we are dealing with a finite or infinite number of D_λ's. $\mathfrak{D}$ is called *open* if all the D_λ's are open sets; a closed covering is specified analogously. If Λ' is a subset of Λ and $\mathfrak{D}' = \{D_\lambda \mid \lambda \in \Lambda'\}$ is also a covering of $\mathfrak{X}$—in other words, the D_λ with $\lambda \in \Lambda'$ already suffice as a covering of $\mathfrak{X}$, then $\mathfrak{D}'$ is called a *subcovering* of $\mathfrak{D}$; one also says that $\mathfrak{D}'$ is contained in $\mathfrak{D}$. A covering $\mathfrak{E} = \{E_\mu \mid \mu \in M\}$ of $\mathfrak{X}$ is called a *refinement* of the covering $\mathfrak{D}$ of $\mathfrak{X}$ if to each $E_\mu \in \mathfrak{E}$ there exists a $D_\lambda \in \mathfrak{D}$ with $E_\mu \subset D_\lambda$. If A is a subset of $\mathfrak{X}$, then one says that the system $\mathfrak{D} = \{D_\lambda \mid \lambda \in \Lambda\}$ of subsets of $\mathfrak{X}$ covers A if $A \subset \bigcup D_\lambda$.

Paraphrasing the Heine-Borel covering theorem on point-sets in R^n, we make the following definition.

16.1 Definition: A topological space $\mathfrak{X}$ and its topology are called *compact* if $\mathfrak{X}$ is Hausdorff and any one of the following equivalent axioms is satisfied:

[*Kp*] *Each open covering of* $\mathfrak{X}$ *possesses a finite subcovering.*

[*Kp'*] *Each system* $\mathfrak{A}$ *of closed subsets of* $\mathfrak{X}$ *with intersection equal to* $\emptyset$ *possesses a finite subsystem with intersection* $\emptyset$.

[*Kp''*] *A system* $\mathfrak{A}$ *of closed subsets of* $\mathfrak{X}$, *each finite subsystem of which has non-empty intersection, itself has non-empty intersection.*

The equivalence of these axioms is immediate. [*Kp'*] is the dual of [*Kp*], [*Kp''*] is a formal reversal of [*Kp'*].

16.2 Definition: A subset A of $\mathfrak{X}$ is called *compact* if A, considered as a subspace, is compact.

As examples of compact spaces, we introduce the following:

(1) Every finite set with any topology.

(2) A convergent sequence including its limit (in the induced topology, of course); one recognizes compactness immediately from the definition of the limit.

(3) In R^n, the compact sets are identical with the sets which are simultaneously closed and bounded.

Concerning example (3), it is namely the Heine-Borel covering theorem from analysis which shows, on the one hand, that these sets are compact, whereas, on the other hand, Theorem 17.2, below, shows that a compact set in R^n is closed so that one sees immediately that an unbounded set in R^n cannot be compact. We shall give an independent proof of this assertion in § 23.

16.3 Theorem: *A subset* $A \subset \mathfrak{X}$ *is compact if, and only if, each covering of* A *by open sets of* $\mathfrak{X}$ *contains a finite subcovering.*

Proof: Let A be compact and suppose the open system $\mathfrak{D} = \{D_\lambda\}$ of sets $D_\lambda \subset \mathfrak{X}$ covers A. Then the traces $(D_\lambda)_A = D_\lambda \cap A$ are A-open and form a covering of A. By [*Kp*], a finite number of these traces $(D_\lambda)_A$ suffice for a covering of A; therefore, also a finite number of the corresponding sets D_λ suffice for a covering of A, which is what we were required to prove.

In an entirely analogous way, one proves the converse by observing that the A-open subsets of A are representable as the traces of $\mathfrak{X}$-open sets.

16.4 Theorem: *For a Hausdorff space $\mathfrak{X}$, the following three properties are equivalent:*

(1) *Each denumerable open covering of $\mathfrak{X}$ possesses a finite subcovering.*

(2) *Each infinite subset A of $\mathfrak{X}$ has at least one accumulation point.*

(3) *Each decreasing sequence $A_1 \supset A_2 \supset \ldots$ of non-empty closed subsets of $\mathfrak{X}$ has non-empty intersection.*

Compact sets have these properties.

Proof: (1) $\Rightarrow$ (2). Let us assume that the infinite set A has no accumulation point. Let $A_0 = \{x_i \mid i = 1, 2, \ldots\}$ be a denumerable subset of A consisting only of distinct points x_i. Also A_0 has no accumulation point; it is therefore closed and hence $\complement A_0$ is open. For each x_i there exists an open neighborhood $U_i \in \mathfrak{U}(x_i)$ which contains no point of A_0 except x_i. $\complement A_0$ and the U_i's form a denumerable open covering of $\mathfrak{X}$, which, by (1), possesses a finite subcovering. But this is obviously impossible and therefore our assumption was false.

(2) $\Rightarrow$ (3). If in a given sequence of non-empty closed sets A_i $(i = 1, 2, \ldots)$ all A_i are equal to one another from some index on, then surely $\bigcap A_i \neq \emptyset$. Otherwise, one can choose a subsequence of mutually distinct A_i; we may assume in advance that $A_i \neq A_{i+1}$. Then one chooses $a_i \in A_i - A_{i+1}$ and by (2) there exists an accumulation point a of the infinite set of a_i's. Since A_i is closed and all the a_j with $j \geqq i$ lie in A_i, we therefore have that $a \in A_i$. Hence, $a \in \bigcap A_i$ which shows that $\bigcap A_i$ is non-empty.

(3) $\Rightarrow$ (1). Let $\mathfrak{D} = \{D_i \mid i = 1, 2, \ldots\}$ be a denumerable open covering of $\mathfrak{X}$. The sets $A_i = \complement(D_1 \cup \ldots \cup D_i)$, $i = 1, 2, \ldots$, form a decreasing sequence of closed sets having intersection $\emptyset$. Hence, according to (3), there certainly is an $A_n = \emptyset$ and therefore $\emptyset = \complement(D_1 \cup \ldots \cup D_n)$, $\mathfrak{X} = D_1 \cup \ldots \cup D_n$, whereby we have constructed a finite subcovering of $\mathfrak{D}$.

Without any further stipulations, condition (1) shows that compact sets have these properties.

A Hausdorff space with the properties (1)–(3) need not be compact. An example of a non-compact Hausdorff space with properties (1)–(3) can be found, say, in the book by Alexandroff-Hopf (see ALEXANDROFF-HOPF [1], page 86). [In the Russian literature and in Alexandroff-Hopf (see ALEXANDROFF-HOPF [1]), compact spaces are designated as "bicompact" whereas Hausdorff spaces with the properties (1)–(3) are called "compact." The "Russian-compact" spaces characterized by the properties (1)–(3) (a more objective and suitable terminology would be "$\aleph_0$-compact") therefore form a somewhat larger class than the compact spaces. For spaces with denumerable weight (Theorem 16.5) and for metric spaces (Theorem 23.2) the two concepts coincide.] But the following theorem holds.

16.5 Theorem: *A Hausdorff space $\mathfrak{X}$ with a denumerable basis, which possesses the properties* (1)–(3) *of the last theorem, is compact.*

Proof: Let $\mathfrak{B} = \{B_i \mid i = 1, 2, \ldots\}$ be a denumerable basis of $\mathfrak{X}$ and let $\mathfrak{D} = \{D_\lambda \mid \lambda \in \Lambda\}$ with arbitrary index set Λ be an open covering of $\mathfrak{X}$. We must construct a finite subcovering of $\mathfrak{X}$.

Every set D_λ is representable as the set-theoretic union of certain basis sets B_i. The system of all the B_i occurring in these representations of D_λ obviously form a denumerable open covering of $\mathfrak{X}$. From this denumerable covering, a finite subsystem $\mathfrak{D}' = \{B_1', \ldots, B_n'\}$ suffices, by (1), to cover $\mathfrak{X}$. Every set B_j' ($j = 1, \ldots, n$) is contained in at least one set D_λ. These n sets D_λ evidently form a finite subcovering of $\mathfrak{D}$.

§ 17. Subspaces of Compact Spaces

The following two theorems form a correlated pair of theorems.

17.1 Theorem: *Every closed subset of a compact space is compact.*

17.2 Theorem: *In a Hausdorff space, every compact subset is closed.*

Proof of Theorem 17.1: Let $\mathfrak{X}$ be compact, $A \subset \mathfrak{X}$, A closed. We appeal to $[Kp']$: Let $\mathfrak{A} = \{A_\lambda \mid \lambda \text{ from an arbitrary index set } \Lambda\}$ be a system of A-closed subsets of A with intersection $\varnothing$. Since A is closed, all the A_λ are also $\mathfrak{X}$-closed (cf. Theorem 6.3, second half). $[Kp']$, applied to $\mathfrak{X}$, asserts that $\mathfrak{A}$ possesses a finite subsystem with intersection $\varnothing$. But this means also that $[Kp']$ is valid for the space A, i.e. that A is compact.

Proof of Theorem 17.2: Let A be a compact set of the Hausdorff space $\mathfrak{X}$. We shall show that $\complement A$ is open. Let $p \notin A$; we shall show that an entire neighborhood of p belongs to $\complement A$. Let x range over the points of A. By $[Hd]$, there exist neighborhoods $U_x \in \mathfrak{U}(x)$, $V_x \in \mathfrak{U}(p)$ with $U_x \cap V_x = \varnothing$. U_x and V_x can be taken as open. A finite number of these U_x, say $U_{x_1}, \ldots, U_{x_n}$, suffice to cover A. We then have that

$$U = \bigcup_{i=1}^{n} U_{x_i}, \; V = \bigcap_{i=1}^{n} V_{x_i}$$

are open and therefore they are neighborhoods of A and p with $U \cap V = \varnothing$. In particular, V is a neighborhood of p which does not intersect A, which is what we were required to prove.

Our proof yielded somewhat more—namely, that A and p possess separated neighborhoods, which fact we shall make use of immediately.

According to the last two theorems, in a compact space the concepts of "closed" and "compact" are equivalent.

17.3 Theorem: *A compact Hausdorff space is normal.*

Proof: We shall first prove regularity and then normality. Let $\mathfrak{X}$ be compact, $A \subset \mathfrak{X}$, A closed, $p \notin A$. We shall prove $[Rg]$: According to Theorem 17.1, A is compact. By the remark at the end of the last proof, there exist neighborhoods U of A and V of p such that $U \cap V = \varnothing$, which is what we had to prove.

Now let A and B be disjoint and closed—therefore, compact in $\mathfrak{X}$. We shall prove $[Nm]$: Let $y \in B$. As above, there exist open neigh-

borhoods U_y of A and V_y of y such that $U_y \cap V_y = \emptyset$. A finite number of the V_y, say $V_{y_1}, \ldots, V_{y_n}$, suffice to cover B.
Then

$$U = \bigcap_{i=1}^{n} U_{y_i} \text{ and } V = \bigcup_{i=1}^{n} V_{y_i}$$

are open neighborhoods of A and B such that $U \cap V = \emptyset$, as is required in [Nm].

17.4 Theorem: *In a Hausdorff space, if A and B are compact then so are $A \cup B$ and $A \cap B$.*

Proof: (1) Let $\mathfrak{D} = \{D_\lambda \mid \lambda$ from an arbitrary index set $\Lambda\}$ be an open covering of $A \cup B$ by means of sets $D_\lambda \subset \mathfrak{X}$ (in the sense of Theorem 16.3). $\mathfrak{D}$ also covers A, and a finite number of the D_λ suffice to cover A. The same holds for B, and therefore a finite number of the D_λ suffice to cover $A \cup B$.

(2) A and B are closed according to Theorem 17.2; $A \cap B$ is an A-closed subset of the compact set A, and moreover by Theorem 17.1 it is compact.

17.5 Theorem: *The product $\mathfrak{X}_0 = \mathfrak{X} \times \mathfrak{Y}$ of two topological spaces $\mathfrak{X} \neq \emptyset, \mathfrak{Y} \neq \emptyset$ is compact if, and only if, both factors $\mathfrak{X}$ and $\mathfrak{Y}$ are compact.*

Proof: First, $\mathfrak{X}_0$ is Hausdorff if, and only if, $\mathfrak{X}$ and $\mathfrak{Y}$ are Hausdorff (cf. Theorem 13.5). Let $\mathfrak{X}_0$ be compact. The projection mappings φ_1 and φ_2 are continuous. According to Theorem 18.1, which we will assume here, $\mathfrak{X}_0$ therefore has compact factors $\mathfrak{X}, \mathfrak{Y}$.

Conversely, let $\mathfrak{X}$ and $\mathfrak{Y}$ be compact. Let $\mathfrak{D} = \{D_\lambda \mid \lambda \in \Lambda\}$ be an open covering of $\mathfrak{X}_0, \Lambda$ a suitable index set. It is to be shown that $\mathfrak{D}$ possesses a finite subcovering. Every D_λ is the union of sets of the form $O = A \times B$ with open $A \subset \mathfrak{X}$ and open $B \subset \mathfrak{Y}$. Let $\mathfrak{O}$ be the set of all these O. $\mathfrak{O}$ is likewise a covering of $\mathfrak{X}_0$, and indeed it is a refinement of $\mathfrak{D}$; it obviously suffices to show that $\mathfrak{O}$ possesses a finite subcovering. Let $x \in \mathfrak{X}$ and $\mathfrak{Y}_x = \{x\} \times \mathfrak{Y}$. $\mathfrak{Y}_x$ is homeomorphic to $\mathfrak{Y}$ and is therefore compact. $\mathfrak{O}$ is also a covering of $\mathfrak{Y}_x$; therefore there exist a finite number of sets $A_i \times B_i$ $(i = 1, \ldots, r)$ from $\mathfrak{D}$ which intersect and cover $\mathfrak{Y}_x$. If we set $A_x = \bigcap A_i$, taken over $i = 1, \ldots, r$, then A_x is an open neighborhood of x and the sets $A_i \times B_i$ also cover $T_x = A_x \times \mathfrak{Y}$. The proof will be finished when we show that $\mathfrak{X}_0$ is covered by a finite number of sets of the form T_x, corresponding to a finite number of points $x \in \mathfrak{X}$. By the procedure described above, there is assigned to each $x \in \mathfrak{X}$ a neighborhood A_x. Because of the compactness of $\mathfrak{X}$, a finite number of the A_x suffice to cover $\mathfrak{X}$. The corresponding finite number of the T_x then cover $\mathfrak{X}_0$. This completes the proof of the theorem.

The theorem carries over without modification to finite products of compact spaces. It holds also in the same form for infinite products (this is the so-called Tikhonov theorem); however, we do not need this generalization in the sequel. Therefore we will not go into the somewhat more difficult proof here which utilizes the well-ordering theorem (see, for instance, J. L. KELLEY [1]).

§ 18. Mappings of Compact Spaces

18.1 Theorem: *If $f: \mathfrak{X} \to \mathfrak{Y}$ is a continuous mapping of a compact space $\mathfrak{X}$ into the Hausdorff space $\mathfrak{Y}$, then the image set $f(\mathfrak{X})$ is compact.*

Proof: Let $\mathfrak{Y}_0 = f(\mathfrak{X})$. Let $\mathfrak{D} = \{D_\lambda \mid \lambda$ from an arbitrary index set $\Lambda\}$ be an open covering of $\mathfrak{Y}_0$. Then the sets $f^{-1}(D_\lambda)$ are open and the system $\{f^{-1}(D_\lambda)\}$ forms an open covering of $\mathfrak{X}$. A finite number of the $f^{-1}(D_\lambda)$ suffices to cover $\mathfrak{X}$ and therefore the corresponding finite number of the D_λ suffices as a cover of $\mathfrak{Y}_0$.

The continuous mappings of a compact space $\mathfrak{X}$ into a Hausdorff space $\mathfrak{Y}$ are therefore closed (cf. the remark on p. 34).

18.2 Theorem: *A monomorphic continuous mapping $f: \mathfrak{X} \to \mathfrak{Y}$ of a compact space $\mathfrak{X}$ into a Hausdorff space $\mathfrak{Y}$ is a homeomorphism of $\mathfrak{X}$ onto a subspace of $\mathfrak{Y}$. A monomorphic continuous mapping f which is also an epimorphism of $\mathfrak{X}$ into $\mathfrak{Y}$ is a homeomorphism of $\mathfrak{X}$ onto $\mathfrak{Y}$; the existence of such a mapping exhibits $\mathfrak{X}$ and $\mathfrak{Y}$ as homeomorphic.*

We shall prove the first part of the theorem; the second part is a special case of it. We must prove the continuity of the inverse mapping $f^{-1}: f(\mathfrak{X}) \to \mathfrak{X}$. Now, f, the inverse mapping to f^{-1}, maps closed sets in $\mathfrak{X}$ into compact, and therefore closed, sets of $f(\mathfrak{X})$ as we have just established. Hence, by the criterion (2′) of Definition 5.4, f^{-1} is continuous.

Let f be a continuous real-valued function on a compact space $\mathfrak{X}$—hence, f is a continuous mapping from $\mathfrak{X}$ into the real line R^1. $f(\mathfrak{X})$ is a compact subset of R^1. $f(\mathfrak{X})$ is bounded because an unbounded subset of R^1 would surely not satisfy the compactness axiom [Kp]; moreover, $f(\mathfrak{X})$ is closed (by Theorem 17.2). Therefore, $f(\mathfrak{X})$ has a finite greatest lower bound a and a finite least upper bound b and these two numbers are themselves function values, $a = f(x)$, $b = f(y)$, where $x, y \in \mathfrak{X}$. Therefore, the following theorem is valid.

18.3 Theorem: *A continuous real-valued function $f(x)$ on a compact set X possesses a finite maximum and a finite minimum, each of which is assumed at at least one point of X. If $f(x)$ is furthermore always positive on X, then there exists a $\delta > 0$ with the property that $f(x) > \delta$ on X.*

§ 19. Locally Compact Spaces. Compactification

19.1 Definition: A topological space $\mathfrak{X}$ is called *locally compact* if it is Hausdorff and each of its points possesses a compact neighborhood.

The real line R^1 and, more generally, R^n are examples.

19.2 Theorem: *A locally compact space $\mathfrak{X}$ is regular.*

Proof: Let $p \in \mathfrak{X}$, A a compact neighborhood of p. If U is an $\mathfrak{X}$-neighborhood of p, then $U_A = U \cap A$ is an A-neighborhood of p and, therefore, because of the regularity of A (by Theorem 17.3, A is even normal), it contains an A-closed A-neighborhood V of p. Since A is $\mathfrak{X}$-closed, V is also $\mathfrak{X}$-closed (see Theorem 6.3, second half); V is the trace of an $\mathfrak{X}$-neighborhood V_0 of p, $V = A \cap V_0$ (Theorem 6.4). Thus, V being the intersection of two $\mathfrak{X}$-neighborhoods is itself an $\mathfrak{X}$-neighborhood. According to the criterion [Rg'], this proves the regularity of $\mathfrak{X}$.

19.3 Theorem: *A locally compact, non-compact space $\mathfrak{X}$ can be embedded in a compact space $\mathfrak{X}' = \mathfrak{X} \cup \{u\}$ by the adjunction of one further point u. More precisely: For a given topology $\mathfrak{T}$ of $\mathfrak{X}$ there exists one and only one topology $\mathfrak{T}'$ on $\mathfrak{X}'$ which is compact and has $\mathfrak{T}$ as its trace.*

As an example of this compactification process, we mention the introduction of the infinitely distant point of the Riemann number sphere in the theory of functions of a complex variable. The significance of this one-point adjunction, as is well known, is rather great.

A. *Uniqueness of* $\mathfrak{T}'$.

In order to prove the existence of a topology $\mathfrak{T}'$ of the required sort, let us first of all assume—following a classical method—the existence of a $\mathfrak{T}'$ and then prove that under this assumption the system $\mathfrak{O}'$ of $\mathfrak{X}'$-open sets is uniquely determined by $\mathfrak{O}$ and u. To this end, we make the resolution $\mathfrak{O}' = \mathfrak{O}_1' \cup \mathfrak{O}_2'$ into the system $\mathfrak{O}_1'$ of those open sets which contain u and the system $\mathfrak{O}_2'$ of those open sets which do not contain u. We first of all assert that $\mathfrak{O}_1'$ *consists of the complementary sets* (*in* $\mathfrak{X}'$) *of compact sets of* $\mathfrak{X}$. Namely, if $O' \in \mathfrak{O}_1'$, then $\complement O'$ is $\mathfrak{X}'$-closed and hence it is compact, according to Theorem 17.1, and does not contain u. Conversely, if A is a compact subset of $\mathfrak{X}$, then A is $\mathfrak{X}'$-closed, by Theorem 17.2, and hence $\complement A$ is $\mathfrak{X}'$-open. Thus, $\mathfrak{O}_1'$ is defined.

We assert further that $\mathfrak{O}_2'$ *consists of the* $\mathfrak{X}$-*open sets of* $\mathfrak{X}$. Namely, if $O' \in \mathfrak{O}_2'$, then the trace in $\mathfrak{X}$—and this is O' itself— is $\mathfrak{X}$-open. Conversely, if O is $\mathfrak{X}$-open, then O is the trace of an $\mathfrak{X}'$-open set O' and therefore $O = O' \cap \mathfrak{X}$. Both factors, O' and $\mathfrak{X}$, are $\mathfrak{X}'$-open and hence O itself is $\mathfrak{X}'$-open. Thus, $\mathfrak{O}_2'$ is defined.

Hence, there exists only one topology $\mathfrak{T}'$ of the desired sort.

B. *Construction of* $\mathfrak{T}'$.

We now omit the assumption in A, above, and construct a set $\mathfrak{O}'$ as the union of two sets $\mathfrak{O}_1'$ and $\mathfrak{O}_2'$ which are defined as in A, above; these definitions are given in italics in A. Using the fundamental formulas (1), (1′) through (3), (3′), one easily verifies that the axioms [O 1] and [O 2] are satisfied so that $\mathfrak{O}'$ really defines a topology $\mathfrak{T}'$ in $\mathfrak{X}'$.

$\mathfrak{T}'$ is Hausdorff; axiom [Hd] holds: For any two points $p, q \in \mathfrak{X}$, this is clear because of the form of $\mathfrak{O}_2'$; for a point $p \in \mathfrak{X}$ and the point u one uses the local compactness at p; a compact neighborhood U of p and its complement $\complement U$ are separating neighborhoods in this case.

That $\mathfrak{T}$ is the trace of $\mathfrak{T}'$ follows directly from the form of $\mathfrak{O}_1'$ and $\mathfrak{O}_2'$.

C. *Compactness of* $\mathfrak{T}'$.

Let $\mathfrak{D} = \{D_\lambda\}$ be an open covering of $\mathfrak{X}'$. u occurs in at least one D_λ say D_0. D_0 belongs to $\mathfrak{O}_1'$ and therefore $\complement D_0$ is compact. A finite number of the D_λ suffice to cover $\complement D_0$. If one also adjoins D_0, then one has a finite number of the D_λ, which cover $\mathfrak{X}'$. Hence, $\mathfrak{T}'$ is, in fact, compact.

Part III

METRIC SPACES

Chapter 6

THEORY OF METRIC SPACES

§ 20. Distance between Points and Distance between Sets

In this chapter, we extend to a fuller theory our earlier (§ 1) and later, incidental remarks about metric spaces. We first of all restrict the definition of continuity.

20.1 Definition: The mapping $f: \mathfrak{X} \to \mathfrak{Y}$ of a metric space $\mathfrak{X}$ into a metric space $\mathfrak{Y}$ is said to be *uniformly continuous* if for arbitrarily given $\varepsilon > 0$ there exists a $\delta = \delta(\varepsilon) > 0$ such that $d(f(x'), f(x)) < \varepsilon$ provided $d(x', x) < \delta$.

One must make positively clear to himself how this differs from the definition of ordinary continuity (Definition 5.3 (1) or Definition 5.4 (1)); the number $\delta = \delta(\varepsilon)$ is uniform, i.e. it can be chosen the same for all $x \in \mathfrak{X}$.

Now and then we also need the concept of continuity and the concept of uniform continuity of functions $f(x, y)$ which assign to each pair x, y of points in $\mathfrak{X}$ a point $p = f(x, y)$ in $\mathfrak{Y}$. Here, in analogy with Definition 20.1, the condition for uniform continuity reads, for instance, as follows:

$$d(f(x', y'), f(x, y)) < \varepsilon \text{ provided } d(x', x) < \delta \text{ and } d(y', y) < \delta.$$

For general topological spaces, it is impossible to define a uniform continuity inasmuch as neighborhoods of distinct points cannot be compared with respect to magnitude. Nonetheless, there is a large class of topological spaces in which this is possible on the basis of special axioms—these are the *uniform spaces* introduced by A. Weil (see N. Bourbaki [1]); but they lie outside the scope of this little book.

20.2 Theorem: *The distance $d(x, y)$ in a metric space is a continuous, even a uniformly continuous, function of both variables x and y.*

The proof follows directly from the triangle inequality (see § 1):

$$| d(x', y') - d(x, y) | \leqq d(x', x) + d(y', y).$$

20.3 Definition: If $A \neq \emptyset$ and $p \in \mathfrak{X}$, then $d(p, A) = \inf d(p,x)$, as x ranges over the set A, is called the *distance from p to A*. If $A \neq \emptyset$, $B \neq \emptyset$, then $d(A, B) = \inf d(x, B) = \inf d(A, y) = \inf d(x, y)$ with arbitrary $x \in A$, $y \in B$, is called the *distance from A to B*.

For $p \in A$, $d(p, A) = 0$, but this situation can also exist when $p \notin A$. For $A \cap B \neq \emptyset$, $d(A, B) = 0$, but this equation can also be valid for $A \cap B = \emptyset$. More precisely, the following theorem is valid.

20.4 Theorem: *$d(p, A) = 0$ if, and only if, $p \in \bar{A}$.*

To prove this, one has only to establish that both facts assert that points of A lie in every ε-neighborhood of p.

Hence, if A is closed, then $p \notin A$ implies that $d(p, A) \neq 0$. But there are disjoint closed sets A, B with $d(A, B) = 0$, for example, the set A of all points of the hyperbola $y = x^{-1}$ in the (x, y)-plane R^2 and the closed fourth quadrant in R^2 as the set B.

20.5 Theorem: *For every subset $A \neq \emptyset$ of $\mathfrak{X}$, $d(x, A)$ is a continuous, even a uniformly continuous, function of x.*

Proof: Let x, x' be arbitrary points of $\mathfrak{X}$. To each $\varepsilon > 0$ there exists a $y = y(\varepsilon) \in A$ such that

$$d(x', y) \leqq d(x', A) + \varepsilon;$$

$$d(x, y) \leqq d(x, x') + d(x', y) \leqq d(x, x') + d(x', A) + \varepsilon.$$

Since $d(x, A) \leqq d(x, y)$, it follows that

$$d(x, A) \leqq d(x, x') + d(x', A) + \varepsilon.$$

Since this is valid for every $\varepsilon > 0$, it holds also for $\varepsilon = 0$:

$$d(x, A) - d(x', A) \leqq d(x, x').$$

This, together with the inequality arising upon the interchange of x and x', yields

$$|\, d(x, A) - d(x', A) \,| \leqq d(x, x'),$$

from which the uniform continuity of $d(x, A)$ follows.

20.6 Theorem: *A metric space is normal.*

We shall prove the axiom [*Nm*]: if A and B are disjoint closed sets, then the sets

$$U = \{x \mid d(x, A) < d(x, B)\}, \; V = \{x \mid d(x, A) > d(x, B)\}$$

are open because of the continuity of $d(x, A)$ and $d(x, B)$ using the same line of reasoning as, say, in Theorem 15.2. For $x \in A$, we have that $d(x, A) = 0$, but $d(x, B) > 0$ by Theorem 20.4. Thus, $A \subset U$ and likewise $B \subset V$. Hence, U and V satisfy the axiom [*Nm*].

We shall now generalize the concept of ε-neighborhood (cf. § 1) $\mathfrak{U}_\varepsilon$ and simultaneously introduce an analogous set $\mathcal{A}_\varepsilon$ by means of the following definition. Let A be an arbitrary subset of $\mathfrak{X}$. Let

$$\mathfrak{U}_\varepsilon(A) = \{x \mid x \in \mathfrak{U}_\varepsilon(p) \text{ for some } p \in A\} = \bigcup_{p \in A} \mathfrak{U}_\varepsilon(p),$$

$$\mathcal{A}_\varepsilon(A) = \{x \mid \mathfrak{U}_\varepsilon(x) \subset A\} = \mathsf{C}(\mathfrak{U}_\varepsilon(\mathsf{C}A)).$$

$\mathfrak{U}_\varepsilon(A)$ contains A, it is open according to the second representation, and therefore it is a neighborhood of A. If $A \neq \varnothing$, then we also have $\mathfrak{U}_\varepsilon(A) \neq \varnothing$.

The equivalence of the two representations of $\mathcal{A}_\varepsilon(A)$ requires proof: We shall show that $\mathsf{C}\mathcal{A}_\varepsilon(A) = \mathfrak{U}_\varepsilon(\mathsf{C}A)$. That a point x belongs to the left member of this equation and hence not to $\mathcal{A}_\varepsilon(A)$ signifies that the ε-sphere about x contains a point $y \in \mathsf{C}A$. This means that x lies in an ε-sphere about y and this signifies that x belongs to the right member. We have thus shown that $\mathsf{C}\mathcal{A}_\varepsilon(A) \subset \mathfrak{U}_\varepsilon\,(\mathsf{C}A)$; that the reverse inclusion holds is proved analogously. The second representation of $\mathcal{A}_\varepsilon(A)$ shows that $\mathcal{A}_\varepsilon(A)$ is *closed*. Obviously, $\mathcal{A}_\varepsilon(A) \subset A$; $\mathcal{A}_\varepsilon(A)$ can be empty even when $A \neq \varnothing$.

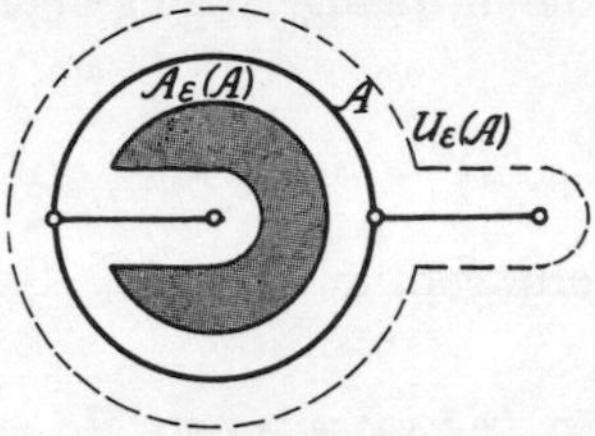

Fig. 4

As an example, we introduce the set A of points (x, y) in R^2 with $x^2 + y^2 \leqq 1$ including the points $(x, 0)$ with $1 \leqq x \leqq 2$ but excluding the points $(x, 0)$ with $-1 \leqq x \leqq 0$. In Fig. 4, $\mathfrak{U}_\varepsilon(A)$ is bounded by the dotted curve and $\mathcal{A}_\varepsilon(A)$ is shown hatched.

We shall now prove some simple facts about $\mathfrak{U}_\varepsilon$ and $\mathcal{A}_\varepsilon$ which will be used later.

20.7 Theorem: $\mathfrak{U}_\varepsilon(\mathcal{A}_\varepsilon(A)) \subset A$; $A \subset \mathcal{A}_\varepsilon(\mathfrak{U}_\varepsilon(A))$.

Proof of the first inclusion: If the point x belongs to $\mathfrak{U}_\varepsilon(\mathcal{A}_\varepsilon(A))$, then we have that $x \in \mathfrak{U}_\varepsilon(y)$ for some $y \in \mathcal{A}_\varepsilon(A)$. But $\mathfrak{U}_\varepsilon(y) \subset A$ and hence x also belongs to A. One proves as easily the second inclusion.

20.8 Theorem: $d(\complement A, \mathcal{A}_\varepsilon(A)) \geqq \varepsilon$ *provided both sets are* $\neq \emptyset$.

Proof: The totality of those points which have a distance $< \varepsilon$ from $\mathcal{A}_\varepsilon(A)$ belongs, according to Theorem 20.7, to A. Thus, every point of $\complement A$ has a distance $\geqq \varepsilon$ from $\mathcal{A}_\varepsilon(A)$.

20.9 Theorem: *In a metric space, every open set O is representable as the union of a denumerable number of closed sets and every closed set A as the intersection of a denumerable number of open sets.*

Proof: Such a representation for an open set O is

$$O = \bigcup_{n=1}^{\infty} \mathcal{A}_{\frac{1}{n}}(O).$$

Namely, if $p \in O$, then also $\mathfrak{U}_{\frac{1}{n}}(p) \subset O$ for suitable n; therefore, every point $p \in O$ occurs in the union. On the other hand, it is clear that the union is contained in O. The second part of the theorem is the dual of the first.

§ 21. Limit Values. Completeness

We shall first show that for metric spaces, in contrast to general topological spaces (see the remark following Definition 13.9) the concepts of limit point and contact point coincide.

21.1 Theorem: *In a metric space, a point p is a contact point of a set A if, and only if, p is a limit point of A.*

One must only prove that a contact point p of A can be represented as the limit of a sequence of points in A. Now for $n = 1, 2, \ldots$ there exists at least one point x_n in each neighborhood $\mathfrak{U}_{\frac{1}{n}}(p)$. The sequence x_n converges to p, which proves the theorem.

21.2 Definition: A sequence $x_1, x_2, \ldots$ is called a *Cauchy sequence* if for each $\varepsilon > 0$ there exists a natural number $n_0 = n_0(\varepsilon)$ such that $d(x_n, x_{n'}) < \varepsilon$ for $n, n' > n_0$.

We note in this definition, which is similar to the definition of uniform continuity at the beginning of the preceding section, that in general topological spaces there is no possibility for defining the concept of a Cauchy sequence.

Every subsequence of a Cauchy sequence is obviously again a Cauchy sequence.

One should not be misled by the theorem usually proved in elementary analysis according to which every Cauchy sequence in the space R^1 of the real numbers is convergent and possesses a limit; this theorem is not valid in arbitrary metric spaces. On the rational line $\mathfrak{Q}$, for example, the sequence of approximating fractions for $\sqrt{2}$ forms a Cauchy sequence which is not convergent in $\mathfrak{Q}$.

A convergent sequence $x_1, x_2, \ldots$ in a metric space is always a Cauchy sequence. Namely, for each $\varepsilon > 0$ there exists an n_0 so that for the limit value x we have that $d(x_n, x) < \frac{\varepsilon}{2}$, $d(x_{n'}, x) < \frac{\varepsilon}{2}$ when $n, n' > n_0$; it follows that $d(x_n, x_{n'}) < \varepsilon$.

21.3 Theorem: *If a Cauchy sequence possesses a convergent subsequence, then the sequence itself converges and has the same limit.*

Proof: Suppose the Cauchy sequence $x_1, x_2, \ldots$ has the subsequence $x_{n_1}, x_{n_2}, \ldots$ which converges to x. For a given $\varepsilon > 0$, there then exists an n_0 with $d(x_{n_i}, x) < \frac{\varepsilon}{2}$ for $n_i > n_0$ and an $\bar{n}_0$ with $d(x_n, x_{n'}) < \frac{\varepsilon}{2}$ for $n, n' > \bar{n}_0$. Therefore, for all $m > n_0$, the inequality

$$d(x_m, x) \leqq d(x_m, x_{n_i}) + d(x_{n_i}, x) < \varepsilon$$

is valid for a suitable $n_i > n_0, \bar{n}_0$.

Thus there are two types of Cauchy sequences—the convergent ones for which every subsequence converges to the same limit and those which do not converge and for which also no subsequence converges. We now make the following definition.

21.4 Definition: The metric space $\mathfrak{X}$ is called *complete* if every Cauchy sequence converges in $\mathfrak{X}$.

The real line R^1 is an example of a complete space; the rational line is an example of a non-complete space.

The following pair of theorems are similar to the two Theorems 17.2 and 17.1.

21.5 Theorem: *In a metric space, a complete subspace is closed.*

21.6 Theorem: *In a complete space, a closed subspace is complete.*

Proof of Theorem 21.5: Let A be a complete subspace of the metric space $\mathfrak{X}$ and let p be an arbitrary point in $\bar{A}$. According to Theorem 21.1, there exists a sequence $x_1, x_2, \ldots$ in A having the limit p. The sequence is Cauchy and has, because of the completeness of A, a limit in A also. Because of the uniqueness of the limit, the latter is equal to p; therefore, $p \in A$. This completes the proof of the theorem.

Proof of Theorem 21.6: Let $\mathfrak{X}$ be a complete space and suppose A is a closed subspace of $\mathfrak{X}$. If $x_1, x_2, \ldots$ is a Cauchy sequence in A, then it has a limit p in $\mathfrak{X}$. Thus, p is a contact point of $A = \bar{A}$, which proves the completeness of A.

It follows from the preceding pair of theorems that in a complete space—for example, on the real line R^1—the concepts "complete" and "closed" coincide.

The following theorem is important for the development of many subareas of topology, and we shall also use it decisively later (in § 35).

21.7 Theorem: (Baire Density Theorem): *Let $\mathfrak{X}$ be a complete space and let B_i, $i = 1, 2, \ldots$, be a denumerable number of dense sets which are open in $\mathfrak{X}$. Then the intersection $\bigcap B_i$ is not empty and it is even dense in $\mathfrak{X}$.*

Proof: Let p be an arbitrary point in $\mathfrak{X}$ and let U_0 be an arbitrary (open) spherical neighborhood of p. Wc shall show that U_0 contains at least one point a from $\bigcap B_i$ and the theorem will thus be proved. $U_0 \cap B_1$ is open and since B_1 is dense this intersection is not empty. We can therefore choose an $a_1 \in U_0 \cap B_1$ and, because of the regularity of $\mathfrak{X}$, there is an open spherical neighborhood U_1 of a_1 such that $\bar{U}_1$ is contained in $U_0 \cap B_1$. Moreover, the radius of U_1 can be chosen smaller than 1. Again, $U_1 \cap B_2$ is open and, because of the density of B_2, this intersection is not empty so that we can choose a_2 and U_2 in a way analogous to that above. Continuing in this manner, for $i = 1, 2, \ldots$, points a_i and spherical neighborhoods U_i can be chosen with the properties that $a_i \in U_i$, $\bar{U}_i \subset U_{i-1} \cap B_i$, and the radius of U_i is smaller than $1/i$.

If n_0 is a natural number and $n, n' > n_0$, then $a_n, a_{n'} \in U_{n_0}$, and therefore we have that $d(a_n, a_{n'}) < 2/n_0$. Thus the sequence $a_1, a_2, \ldots$ is Cauchy and has a limit a in the complete space $\mathfrak{X}$. The subsequence $a_i, a_{i+1}, \ldots$ also has the limit a. All its terms are contained in $\bar{U}_i$ and, since $\overline{U}_i$ is closed, a is also contained in $\overline{U}_i$. This means that $a \in \overline{U}_i \subset U_{i-1} \cap B_i \subset B_i$ and $a \in U_0$. Thus, we have that also $a \in \bigcap B_i$, which is what we were required to prove.

One can show that for each metric space $\mathfrak{X}$ there exists a complete space $\hat{\mathfrak{X}}$ which contains $\mathfrak{X}$. The construction of $\hat{\mathfrak{X}}$ from $\mathfrak{X}$ proceeds according to the pattern of the well-known Cantor-Méray procedure for the construction of the real numbers from the rational numbers with the aid of rational Cauchy sequences (which are also called fundamental sequences). This construction is of basic importance for many areas of mathematics. We shall first formulate this fact somewhat more exactly.

21.8 Theorem: *Each metric space $\mathfrak{X}$ can be embedded in a complete space $\hat{\mathfrak{X}}$; more specifically, to each metric space $\mathfrak{X}$ there exists a complete space $\hat{\mathfrak{X}}$ which contains $\mathfrak{X}$ as a subspace and in which $\mathfrak{X}$ is dense. $\hat{\mathfrak{X}}$ is uniquely determined up to isometry by these two requirements.*

Since we do not need this theorem in the sequel, we shall not carry out the rather wearisome proof in detail, but rather only give six individual steps in the proof, each of which is not too difficult to prove.

(1) Two Cauchy sequences $x_1, x_2, \ldots$ and $y_1, y_2, \ldots$ are said to be equivalent if the real sequence $d(x_n, y_n)$ is a null sequence; let $\hat{\mathfrak{X}}$ be the set of equivalence classes.

(2) One defines a metric in $\hat{\mathfrak{X}}$ by assigning the distance $d = \lim d(y_n, x_n)$ to two arbitrary Cauchy sequences which are denoted as above. We have to show that this limit exists and depends only on the equivalence class of the Cauchy sequences and further that the axioms [M 1]–[M 3] are satisfied. $\hat{\mathfrak{X}}$ thus becomes a metric space.

(3) $\hat{\mathfrak{X}}$ contains the subspace $\mathfrak{X}_0$ of constant sequences—more specifically, those equivalence classes which contain the constant sequences. $\mathfrak{X}_0$ is isometric to $\mathfrak{X}$ and can be identified with $\mathfrak{X}$ so that $\mathfrak{X} \subset \hat{\mathfrak{X}}$ holds.

(4) $\hat{\mathfrak{X}}$ is complete. In order to show this, we must form a Cauchy sequence of Cauchy sequences of $\mathfrak{X}$ and prove it converges in the sense of the metric just introduced. We obtain the limit as the diagonal sequence from the sequences at hand.

(5) $\mathfrak{X}$ is dense in $\hat{\mathfrak{X}}$.

(6) Uniqueness: Two spaces $\hat{\mathfrak{X}}_1$ and $\hat{\mathfrak{X}}_2$ of the type specified in the theorem are isometric.

§ 22. Diameter. Boundedness

22.1 Definition: If $A \neq \emptyset$ is a subset of a metric space $\mathfrak{X}$, then the least upper bound

$d(A) = \sup d(x,y)$, taken over arbitrary $x, y \in A$, (provided it is finite) is called the *diameter* $d(A)$ of A, and, in this case, A is said to be *bounded*. If the least upper bound is not finite, then A is said to be *unbounded*.

$d(A) = 0$ means that A consists of only one point.

The diameter of a triangle in R^2 is equal to the length of its longest side (also see Theorem 29.2, below).

22.2 Theorem: *For every set* $A \neq \emptyset$, *we have that* $d(\bar{A}) = d(A)$.

Proof: Certainly $d(\bar{A}) \geqq d(A)$. Let $x, y \in \bar{A}$; then for every $\varepsilon > 0$ there exist points $x', y' \in A$ such that $d(x, x') < \varepsilon$ and $d(y, y') < \varepsilon$ so that $d(x, y) \leqq d(x, x') + d(x', y') + d(y', y) < d(x', y') + 2\varepsilon \leqq d(A) + 2\varepsilon$. Since this holds for every $\varepsilon > 0$, it follows that $d(x, y) \leqq d(A)$ and therefore $d(\bar{A}) = \sup d(x, y) \leqq d(A)$. This completes the proof of the theorem.

A covering $\mathfrak{D} = \{D_\lambda \mid \lambda$ from an arbitrary index set $\Lambda\}$ of a space $\mathfrak{X}$ or of a set $A \subset \mathfrak{X}$ is called an ε-covering provided all the $d(D_\lambda)$ are $< \varepsilon$.

22.3 Definition: A set $A \subset \mathfrak{X}$ is called *totally bounded* if it allows a finite ε-covering for every $\varepsilon > 0$.

A totally bounded set A is also bounded. Namely, if for any fixed $\varepsilon > 0$, $\mathfrak{D} = \{D_i \mid i = 1, \ldots, m\}$ is a finite ε-covering of A, a_i is a fixed point in D_i, and $d = \operatorname{Max} d(a_i, a_k)$ for $i, k = 1, \ldots, m$, then $d(x, y) \leqq d(x, a_i) + d(a_i, a_k) + d(a_k, y) \leqq d + 2\varepsilon$ holds for any two points $x, y \in A$ and suitable i and k.

On the other hand, a bounded set need not be totally bounded, as the set of unit points $\mathfrak{e}_i = (0, \ldots, 0, 1, 0, \ldots)$ (1 in the i-th place) in Hilbert space shows. This set has the diameter $\sqrt{2}$ but admits no finite 1-covering.

22.4 Theorem: *The metric space $\mathfrak{X}$ is totally bounded if, and only if, every sequence in $\mathfrak{X}$ has a Cauchy subsequence.*

Proof: First, let $\mathfrak{X}$ be totally bounded. We start with an arbitrary sequence $x_1, x_2, \ldots$. For $n = 1, 2, \ldots$, we consider the finite $(1/n)$-coverings $\mathfrak{D}_n$ of $\mathfrak{X}$. At least one of the finitely many sets of $\mathfrak{D}_1$ contains an infinite number of terms of the sequence; let these be (in the new notation) the points of the subsequence

$$(1) \qquad x_1^{(1)}, x_2^{(1)}, x_3^{(1)}, \ldots.$$

This sequence, or more precisely the set of the points of this sequence, has diameter < 1. At least one of the finite number of sets of $\mathfrak{D}_2$ contains an infinite number of terms of the sequence (1); let these be, again in the new notation, the points of the subsequence of (1)

$$(2) \qquad x_1^{(2)}, x_2^{(2)}, x_3^{(2)}, \ldots.$$

This sequence has diameter $< \frac{1}{2}$. Continuing further in this manner, we obtain a sequence (n) for every natural number n; if $n > n'$, then the sequence (n) is a subsequence of the sequence (n') and all sequences are subsequences of the initial sequence. The sequence (n) has diameter $< \frac{1}{n}$. We now assert that the diagonal sequence

$$x_1^{(1)}, x_2^{(2)}, x_3^{(3)}, \ldots$$

is a Cauchy subsequence of the initial sequence. In any case, the subsequence beginning with $x_k^{(k)}$ is a subsequence of the sequence (k) and therefore it has diameter $< \frac{1}{k}$. Hence, if $n, n' > n_0$, then it follows that $d(x_n^{(n)}, x_{n'}^{(n')}) < \frac{1}{n_0}$ and this completes the proof of our assertion and hence the first part of the theorem.

Conversely, suppose $\mathfrak{X}$ is not totally bounded. Then, for sufficiently small $\varepsilon = \varepsilon_0$, there exists no finite ε-covering of $\mathfrak{X}$. Choose the point a_1 arbitrarily in $\mathfrak{X}$. The $\left(\frac{\varepsilon}{3}\right)$-neighborhood of a_1 has diameter $< \varepsilon$ and hence it cannot cover all of $\mathfrak{X}$. Let a_2 be chosen outside this neighborhood. The union of the two $\left(\frac{\varepsilon}{3}\right)$-neighborhoods of a_1 and a_2 cannot cover all of $\mathfrak{X}$. Hence an a_3 can be chosen situated outside this union. Continuing further in this manner, we choose a sequence $a_1, a_2, \ldots$ in which every two points have a distance $\geqq \frac{\varepsilon}{3}$. Such a sequence obviously has no Cauchy subsequence; this proves the second part of the theorem.

Chapter 7

COMPACTA

§ 23. Characteristics of Compacta

23.1 Definition: A compact metric space is called a *compactum.*

23.2 Theorem: *A compactum can also be described as a metric space* $\mathfrak{X}$ *which satisfies any one of the following three equivalent conditions.*

(1) *Every denumerable open covering of* $\mathfrak{X}$ *possesses a finite subcovering.*

(2) *Every infinite subset of* $\mathfrak{X}$ *has at least one accumulation point.*

(3) *Every decreasing sequence* $A_1 \supset A_2 \supset \ldots$ *of non-empty closed subsets of* $\mathfrak{X}$ *has a non-empty intersection.*

Proof: That a compactum has these properties was established earlier (see Theorem 16.4). In order to show, conversely, that each of the properties (1)–(3) implies the compactness of $\mathfrak{X}$, it suffices, according to Theorem 16.5, to show that a metric space $\mathfrak{X}$ with the property (2) possesses a denumerable basis. To this end, we choose an $\varepsilon > 0$; the existence of infinitely many points $a_i \in \mathfrak{X}$ with $d(a_i, a_j) \geqq \varepsilon$ $(i, j = 1, 2, \ldots)$ would obviously contradict (2) and, therefore, there exists a finite number of points a_i $(i = 1, \ldots, k)$ such that every point $x \in \mathfrak{X}$ has a distance $d(x, a_i) < \varepsilon$ from at least one a_i. Such a finite system of points is called an ε-*net*. If for each $\varepsilon = \frac{1}{n}$ $(n = 1, 2, \ldots)$, we choose an ε-net, then we obtain in all a denumerable set which is dense in $\mathfrak{X}$. By Theorem 10.7, $\mathfrak{X}$ thus has a denumerable basis, which is what we were required to prove.

23.3 Theorem: *A compactum can also be described as a metric space with the property that every sequence of points in $\mathfrak{X}$ has a convergent subsequence.*

Proof: Let $\mathfrak{X}$ be a compactum and suppose $x_i (i = 1, 2, \ldots)$ is a sequence of points in $\mathfrak{X}$. Either there are a finite number of distinct points x_i, in which case one of them occurs infinitely often in the sequence and represents a convergent subsequence, or we can select from the sequence of the points x_i a subsequence consisting of distinct points and then directly assume that the x_i themselves are distinct. They form an infinite set which, because of the compactness of $\mathfrak{X}$, has an accumulation point p. If we choose for $n = 1, 2, \ldots$ one x_i in each of the neighborhoods $\mathfrak{U}_{\frac{1}{n}}(p)$, then the subsequence of the x_i so chosen converges to p, and the property of the theorem is therefore proved.

Conversely, suppose the metric space $\mathfrak{X}$ has the property of the theorem. If A is an infinite set, then one can select from A a sequence $x_i (i = 1, 2, \ldots)$ consisting of distinct points which then has a subsequence which converges to a point p. Thus, p is an accumulation point of the set of the x_i and hence an accumulation point of A. Therefore, $\mathfrak{X}$ is compact according to condition (2) of the preceding theorem.

23.4 Theorem: *A metric space $\mathfrak{X}$ is a compactum if, and only if, it is complete and totally bounded.*

Proof: Let $\mathfrak{X}$ be a compactum. The preceding theorem shows that every sequence from $\mathfrak{X}$ always has a Cauchy subsequence, which according to Theorem 22.4 means that $\mathfrak{X}$ is totally bounded. By the preceding theorem, a Cauchy sequence has a convergent subsequence and hence it itself converges (see Theorem 21.3); this means that $\mathfrak{X}$ is complete.

Conversely, if $\mathfrak{X}$ is complete and totally bounded, then every sequence has a Cauchy subsequence (by Theorem 22.4) and this Cauchy subsequence converges. Thus, $\mathfrak{X}$ is compact (see Theorem 23.3).

For the real space R^n, this theorem asserts that in R^n the complete sets are identical with the closed sets (cf. Theorems 21.5, 21.6 and the attached remark), and that the compacta in R^n are identical with the bounded closed sets, which proves a result already obtained along the way in § 16.

We note further that the Hilbert cube $\mathfrak{P}$ (cf. example (b) in § 1) is compact. Since, according to § 12, $\mathfrak{P}$ is homeomorphic to the infinite product I^∞ of a denumerable number of unit segments, which is compact by the Tikhonov theorem (which we did not prove) (see end of § 17), our assertion that the Hilbert cube $\mathfrak{P}$ is compact follows. An independent proof can be given by proving the completeness of the Hilbert space H and the total boundedness of $\mathfrak{P}$. Both can be proved without any particular difficulty.

§ 24. Distance, Coverings and Connectivity

24.1 Theorem: *The following assertions are valid for arbitrary subsets $A \neq \emptyset$, $B \neq \emptyset$ of a metric space $\mathfrak{X}$:*

(1) *If A is compact, B arbitrary, then there exists a point $p \in A$ such that $d(A, B) = d(p, B)$.*

(2) *If A is compact, B closed, $A \cap B = \emptyset$, then $d(A, B) > 0$.*

(3) *If A and B are compact, then there exist points $p \in A, q \in B$ such that $d(A, B) = d(p, q)$.*

(4) *If A is compact, then there exist points $x_0, y_0 \in A$ such that $d(A) = d(x_0, y_0)$.*

Proof: (1) d is a continuous real-valued function (Theorem 20.5) on the compact set A. By Theorem 18.3, it takes on its minimum value $d(p, B)$ for at least one point $p \in A$.

(2) $d(p, B) = 0$ would mean (by Theorem 20.4) that $p \in B$, contrary to the assumption that $A \cap B = \emptyset$.

(3) d is a continuous real-valued function on the compact space $A \times B$ (Theorem 17.5). It takes on its minimum value $d(p,q)$ for at least one point (p,q) in $A \times B$. We then have that $d(p,q) = d(A, B)$.

(4) Analogous statements hold for the maximum value of the function d on the compact set $A \times A$.

24.2 Theorem: (The Lebesgue Lemma): *For every open covering* $\mathfrak{D} = \{D_\lambda \mid \lambda$ *from an arbitrary index set* $\Lambda\}$ *of a compactum* $\mathfrak{X}$ *there exists a real number* $r > 0$ *such that every set* $A \subset \mathfrak{X}$ *with diameter* $d(A) < r$ *is contained entirely in one set* D_λ. (Every number of this sort is called a *Lebesgue number* of $\mathfrak{D}$).

Proof: Suppose such an r did not exist. Then for each $r = \frac{1}{k}(k = 1, 2, \ldots)$ there exists a set A_k with $d(A_k) < \frac{1}{k}$ which is not contained entirely in one D_λ. In each A_k we choose a point a_k and search for the limit a of a convergent subsequence of the sequence of the a_k. The limit a lies in a set D_λ and also an entire ε-neighborhood $\mathfrak{U}_\varepsilon(a)$ with suitable $\varepsilon > 0$ is contained in this D_λ. For all k, for which (1) $d(a_k, a) < \frac{\varepsilon}{2}$, (2) $\frac{1}{k} < \frac{\varepsilon}{2}$, a_k and A_k lie entirely in D_λ, contrary to our assumption.

24.3 Theorem: *In a compactum* $\mathfrak{X}$, *for each system* $\mathfrak{A} = \{A_\lambda \mid \lambda$ *from an arbitrary index set* $\Lambda\}$ *of closed sets* A_λ *with intersection* $\bigcap A_\lambda = \emptyset$ *there exists an* $\varepsilon > 0$ *such that the system* $\mathfrak{A}_\varepsilon$ *and the system* $\overline{\mathfrak{A}}_\varepsilon$, where

$$\mathfrak{A}_\varepsilon = \{B_\lambda = \mathfrak{U}_\varepsilon(A_\lambda) \mid \lambda \in \Lambda\}, \overline{\mathfrak{A}}_\varepsilon = \{\overline{B}_\lambda = \overline{\mathfrak{U}_\varepsilon(A_\lambda)} \mid \lambda \in \Lambda\},$$

also have intersection $\bigcap B_\lambda = \emptyset$ *and* $\bigcap \overline{B}_\lambda = \emptyset$.

Proof: It suffices to prove the assertion $\bigcap \overline{B}_\lambda = \emptyset$. Suppose that there existed no ε of the required sort. Then, for every $\varepsilon = \frac{1}{k}$ $(k = 1, 2, \ldots)$, the sets $\overline{B}_\lambda$ of the system $\overline{\mathfrak{A}}_{\frac{1}{k}}$ have an intersection which contains at least one point a_k. The sequence of the points a_k possesses in the compactum $\mathfrak{X}$ at least one convergent subsequence which converges to a point a. The points a_k and all the a_e with $e > k$ belong to the intersection of the sets of $\overline{\mathfrak{A}}_{\frac{1}{k}}$ and therefore the same holds for a. Then the following assertion holds for every index $\lambda \in \Lambda$: In every $\left(\frac{2}{k}\right)$-neighborhood of a there lie points of A_λ. Because of the fact that

A_λ is closed, a therefore also lies in A_λ. Hence a also belongs to the intersection $\bigcap A_\lambda$, contrary to the assumption that $\bigcap A_\lambda = \varnothing$. This completes the proof of the theorem.

For compacta, the concept of connectivity can be stated in a somewhat simpler way than for arbitrary spaces. We first make a definition: If $\varepsilon > 0$ is a real number, then two points x, y of a metric space $\mathfrak{X}$ are said to be *ε-chained* if there exists a finite sequence of points $x = x_0$, $x_1, \ldots, x_n = y$ in $\mathfrak{X}$ such that $d(x_{i-1}, x_i) < \varepsilon$; $i = 1, \ldots, n$. For each fixed $\varepsilon > 0$ the existence of an ε-chain yields an equivalence relation among the points of $\mathfrak{X}$. The classes of ε-chained points are called *ε-components* C_ε of $\mathfrak{X}$; each point $x \in \mathfrak{X}$ lies in one and only one of the ε-components $C_\varepsilon = C_\varepsilon(x)$, which contains all the points of $\mathfrak{X}$ which are ε-chained to x. The ε-components C_ε are open; for, together with each $x \in C_\varepsilon$ also all the points of the spherical neighborhood $\mathfrak{U}_\varepsilon(x)$ obviously belong to C_ε. The sets C_ε are also closed because $\complement C_\varepsilon$ is the union of all the ε-components of $\mathfrak{X}$ which are different from C_ε and hence it is the union of open sets and therefore it is itself open. The C_ε are therefore open-closed. Now if $\mathfrak{X}$ is connected, $\mathfrak{X}$ can contain only a single ε-component, namely itself. This proves the following theorem.

24.4 Theorem: *In a connected metric space, every pair of points are ε-chained for every $\varepsilon > 0$.*

For compact spaces $\mathfrak{X}$, this theorem has a converse and yields the above-mentioned criterion for a space to be connected.

24.5 Theorem: *A compactum $\mathfrak{X}$ is connected if, and only if, every pair of its points are ε-chained for every $\varepsilon > 0$.*

It is sufficient to show that in a compactum $\mathfrak{X}$ which is not connected, the condition of the theorem is not satisfied, i.e. that there exist points x, y in $\mathfrak{X}$ and a real number $\varepsilon > 0$ such that x and y are not ε-chained. In fact, if $\mathfrak{X}$ is not connected, then there exists a partition $\mathfrak{X} = X_1 \cup X_2$. X_1 and X_2 are compact and we have that $d(X_1, X_2) = \varepsilon > 0$ (Theorem 24.1 (2)). Obviously, no point of X_1 is ε-chained to a point of X_2. This completes the proof of the theorem.

The space of rational numbers (which is not connected) shows that the theorem is not valid in general for metric spaces.

24.6 Theorem: *In a compactum $\mathfrak{X}$, the connectivity component $C(x)$ of a point x is identical with the intersection $D(x)$ of all the open-closed subsets of $\mathfrak{X}$ which contain x and identical with the intersection $D'(x)$ of all ε-components $C_\varepsilon(x)$ for all $\varepsilon > 0$.*

Proof: Evidently, $C(x) \subset D(x) \subset D'(x)$ (even for arbitrary metric spaces). It suffices to show that $C(x) \supset D'(x)$. When ε_i $(i = 1, 2, \ldots)$ is a monotonically decreasing null sequence and if $F = F(x) = \bigcap C_{\varepsilon_i}(x)$, then it suffices to simply show that $C(x) \supset F$. To this end, it finally suffices, because of the maximality property of the component $C(x)$, to prove that the set F is connected. In order to show this indirectly, we assume that F is not connected. Then there exist in F, considered as a subspace, non-empty disjoint closed subsets A, B with $F = A \cup B$. Since the $C_{\varepsilon_i}(x)$ and hence also F are closed, we have that A and B are also $\mathfrak{X}$-closed and compact, and we have that $d(A, B) = \varepsilon > 0$. Suppose the point x lies, say, in A, and let y be an arbitrary point in B. We form

$$U = \mathfrak{U}_{\frac{\varepsilon}{4}}(A),\ V = \mathfrak{U}_{\frac{\varepsilon}{4}}(B),\ G = \mathfrak{X} - (U \cup V).$$

We have that $d(U, V) \geqq \frac{\varepsilon}{2}$. Now, x and y are ε_i-chained for every ε_i. Whenever ε_i is $< \frac{\varepsilon}{2}$, G must obviously contain a point of a sequence of points joining x and y with the distance between successive points of this sequence $< \varepsilon_i$. Hence, $G \cap C_{\varepsilon_i}(x) \neq \emptyset$, whenever $\varepsilon_i < \frac{\varepsilon}{2}$. The closed monotonically decreasing sets $G \cap C_{\varepsilon_i}(x)$ have an intersection which is different from $\emptyset$ (see Theorem 23.2):

$$\emptyset \neq \bigcap(G \cap C_{\varepsilon_i}(x)) = G \cap (\bigcap C_{\varepsilon_i}(x)) = G \cap F,$$

which contradicts the definition of $F = A \cup B$. This completes the proof of the theorem.

However, in general, $C(x) \neq D(x) \neq D'(x)$ holds for spaces $\mathfrak{X}$ which are not compact.

24.7 Definition: A non-empty connected compactum is called a *continuum*. If it contains more than one point, it is called a *proper* continuum.

Examples of continua are the finite closed intervals of R^1 and also the bounded closed connected subsets of R^n.

The image of a continuum under a continuous mapping into a metric space is again a continuum (see Theorems 7.4 and 18.1).

Concerning continua, we prove the following theorem.

24.8 Theorem: *A proper continuum* $\mathfrak{X}$ *has the cardinality* $\mathfrak{c}$ *of the continuum.*

Proof: A continuum $\mathfrak{X}$, being a compactum, has a denumerable basis (cf. Theorem 23.2, Proof), i.e the system of closed sets of $\mathfrak{X}$ therefore has at most the cardinality $\mathfrak{c}$ (Theorem 10.8). The same therefore holds for the subsystem of all one-point subsets of $\mathfrak{X}$, i.e. for $\mathfrak{X}$ itself.

On the other hand, we can construct a subset of $\mathfrak{X}$ having the cardinality $\mathfrak{c}$: Let $p_0, p_1, p_0 \neq p_1$, be two points of $\mathfrak{X}$; let U_0 and U_1 be spherical neighborhoods of p_0 and p_1 respectively with a radius $< \frac{1}{2}$ and with $\overline{U}_0 \cap \overline{U}_1 = \emptyset$. For every $\varepsilon > 0$, p_0 and p_1 are ε-chained; from this we can conclude that U_0 contains, besides p_0, at least one more point $p_{01} \neq p_{00} = p_0$. Let $U_{00} \subset U_0$ and $U_{01} \subset U_0$ be spherical neighborhoods of p_{00} and p_{01} respectively with a radius $< \frac{1}{2^2}$ and with $\overline{U}_{00} \cap \overline{U}_{01} = \emptyset$.

Analogously, let $U_{10} \subset U_1$ and $U_{11} \subset U_1$ with a diameter $< \frac{1}{2^2}$ and with $\overline{U}_{10} \cap \overline{U}_{11} = \emptyset$ be determined. Continuing further this way, we obtain for every natural number $r = 1, 2, \ldots, 2^r$ non-empty disjoint closed sets $\overline{U}_{i_1 \ldots i_r}$ with $d(\overline{U}_{i_1 \ldots i_r}) < \frac{1}{2^r}$ and $\overline{U}_{i_1 \ldots i_r i_{r+1}} \subset \overline{U}_{i_1 \ldots i_r}$, where the indices $i_1, i_2, \ldots$ are either 0 or 1. For every such infinite sequence $i_1, i_2, \ldots$ there exists a nested sequence of closed sets whose diameters form a null sequence, i.e. there results a well-defined point in $\mathfrak{X}$. Distinct sequences obviously correspond to distinct points of $\mathfrak{X}$. Since the set of all such sequences has the cardinality $\mathfrak{c}$, this proves the existence of a subset of $\mathfrak{X}$ having the cardinality $\mathfrak{c}$. This completes the proof of the theorem.

§ 25. Mappings of Compacta

We first recall that a continuous image of a compact space is compact (see Theorem 18.1) and generalize this assertion now to compacta.

25.1 Theorem: *A continuous mapping f of a compactum $\mathfrak{X}$ into a metric space is uniformly continuous.*

Proof: Let $\varepsilon > 0$ be given. For every $x \in \mathfrak{X}$, let U_x denote the δ_x-neighborhood of x which is determined by a δ_x with the property that

$$d(f(x'), f(x)) < \varepsilon \text{ provided } d(x', x) < \delta_x.$$

The totality of all U_x forms an open covering of $\mathfrak{X}$. Let r be a Lebesgue number of this covering (see Theorem 24.2). If $x_1, x_2 \in \mathfrak{X}$ and $d(x_1, x_2) < r$, then x_1, x_2 lie in *one* neighborhood U_x; i.e., there exists an $x \in \mathfrak{X}$ such that $x_1, x_2 \in U_x$. Then we have that

$$d(f(x_1), f(x_2)) \leqq d(f(x_1), f(x)) + d(f(x), f(x_2)) < 2\varepsilon,$$

which proves the uniform continuity of f inasmuch as r depends only on the covering—therefore only on ε—and not on the point $x \in \mathfrak{X}$.

We shall now prove several simple facts about function spaces. Let $\mathfrak{X}$ be a compactum, $\mathfrak{Y}$ a metric space, and f, g two continuous mappings of $\mathfrak{X}$ into $\mathfrak{Y}$. $d(f(x), g(x))$ is a continuous real-valued function on $\mathfrak{X}$ and hence has a finite maximum which it takes on at at least one point of $\mathfrak{X}$. We set (as in § 1, example (c')) $d(f, g) = \text{Max } d(f(x), g(x))$, where Max is taken over all $x \in \mathfrak{X}$. Thus the set of all continuous mappings of $\mathfrak{X}$ into $\mathfrak{Y}$ becomes a metric space $\mathfrak{F}(\mathfrak{X}, \mathfrak{Y})$. The validity of axioms [M 1] and [M 2] is immediate; one proves the triangle axiom [M 3] as in § 1, example (c').

25.2 Theorem: *If $\mathfrak{X}$ is a compactum and $\mathfrak{Y}$ is complete, then $\mathfrak{F}(\mathfrak{X}, \mathfrak{Y})$ is complete.*

Proof: Let $f_1, f_2, \ldots$ be a Cauchy sequence in $\mathfrak{F}(\mathfrak{X}, \mathfrak{Y})$. We must show that it possesses a limit in $\mathfrak{F}(\mathfrak{X}, \mathfrak{Y})$. For every $\varepsilon > 0$, an $n_0 =$

$n_0(\varepsilon)$ can be found such that $d(f_n(x), f_{n'}(x)) \leqq d(f_n, f_{n'}) < \varepsilon$ for all n, $n' > n_0$ and all x. Therefore, for every fixed $x \in \mathfrak{X}, f_1(x), f_2(x), \ldots$ is a Cauchy sequence in the complete space $\mathfrak{Y}$. Denote its limit by $f(x)$. We shall prove that f is continuous at every point $x = x_0 \in \mathfrak{X}$ and that it is a limit value of our Cauchy sequence; this will then complete the proof of the theorem.

The sequence $f_{n'}(x)$ is convergent to $f(x)$; therefore, because of the continuity of the distance function d, the sequence $d(f_n(x), f_{n'}(x))$ is convergent to $d(f_n(x), f(x))$. From the last inequality, i.e. $d(f_n(x), f_{n'}(x)) \leqq d(f_n, f_{n'}) < \varepsilon$ it therefore follows upon this passage to the limit that

$$d(f_n(x), f(x)) \leqq \varepsilon \text{ for all } n > n_0 \text{ and all } x.$$

(This signifies the "uniform convergence" of the image sequence $f_1(x), f_2(x), \ldots$ to $f(x)$, from which we deduce the continuity of f in the well-known way.) We have that

$$d(f(x), f(x_0)) \leqq d(f(x), f_n(x)) + d(f_n(x), f_n(x_0)) + d(f_n(x_0), f(x_0)).$$

According to what we have already proved, the first and third summands are $\leqq \varepsilon$ provided $n > n_0$ for arbitrary x; the middle summand is smaller than ε provided $d(x, x_0) < \delta$ because of the continuity of f_n. Thus, $d(f(x), f(x_0)) < 3\varepsilon$ for $d(x, x_0) < \delta$, and this means that f is continuous at x_0.

The uniform convergence proved above now shows that f is the limit value of the sequence $f_1, f_2, \ldots$ in $\mathfrak{F}(\mathfrak{X}, \mathfrak{Y})$.

25.3 Definition: If $\varepsilon > 0$ and $f: \mathfrak{X} \to \mathfrak{Y}$ is a continuous mapping of the metric space $\mathfrak{X}$ into the metric space $\mathfrak{Y}$, then f is called an ε-*mapping* provided $d(f^{-1}(y)) < \varepsilon$ for all $y \in f(\mathfrak{X})$.

For an ε-mapping, it therefore follows from $f(x_1) = f(x_2)$ that $d(x_1, x_2) < \varepsilon$, or, expressed differently, that $d(x_1, x_2) \geqq \varepsilon$ implies that $f(x_1) \neq f(x_2)$. But we note that the satisfaction of the definition condition $d(f^{-1}(y)) < \varepsilon$ still does not completely suffice to guarantee that f is monomorphic. The ε-mappings surely are a forerunner to the monomorphic mappings. We denote the space of all ε-mappings of the compactum $\mathfrak{X}$ into the metric space $\mathfrak{Y}$ by $\mathfrak{F}_\varepsilon(\mathfrak{X}, \mathfrak{Y})$. Then $\bigcap \mathfrak{F}_\varepsilon(\mathfrak{X}, \mathfrak{Y})$, taken over all $\varepsilon > 0$ or over all $\varepsilon = \dfrac{1}{n}$ $(n = 1, 2, \ldots)$, is equal to the space of monomorphic continuous mappings of $\mathfrak{X}$ into $\mathfrak{Y}$.

25.4 Theorem: *For every ε-mapping f of the compactum $\mathfrak{X}$ into the metric space $\mathfrak{Y}$, there exists an $\eta > 0$ with the property that $d(f(x_1), f(x_2)) < \eta$ implies $d(x_1, x_2) < \varepsilon$.*

We shall prove that $d(x_1, x_2) \geqq \varepsilon$ implies that $d(f(x_1), f(x_2)) \geqq \eta > 0$. The set A of points (x_1, x_2) of the compact space $\mathfrak{X} \times \mathfrak{X}$ with $d(x_1, x_2) \geqq \varepsilon$ is closed and therefore compact. The function d is positive, real-valued and continuous on A. This yields the existence of an $\eta > 0$ of the desired sort (cf. Theorem 18.3).

25.5 Theorem: *If $\mathfrak{X}$ is a compactum and $\mathfrak{Y}$ is an arbitrary metric space, then $\mathfrak{F}_\varepsilon(\mathfrak{X}, \mathfrak{Y})$ is obviously an open subspace of $\mathfrak{F}(\mathfrak{X}, \mathfrak{Y})$.*

Proof: Let $f \in \mathfrak{F}_\varepsilon(\mathfrak{X}, \mathfrak{Y})$ and $d(f, g) < \dfrac{\eta}{2}$ with the real number $\eta > 0$ from the preceding theorem. We shall show that g is also an ε-mapping; the theorem will then be proved. Let us assume for $x_1, x_2 \in \mathfrak{X}$ that $g(x_1) = g(x_2) = y$. It then follows that

$$d(f(x_1), f(x_2)) \leqq d(f(x_1), g(x_1)) + d(g(x_1), g(x_2)) + d(g(x_2), f(x_2))$$

$$< \frac{\eta}{2} + 0 + \frac{\eta}{2} = \eta.$$

It follows from the preceding theorem that $d(x_1, x_2) < \varepsilon$. From this one can at first only deduce that $d(g^{-1}(y)) \leqq \varepsilon$. But now $g^{-1}(y)$, as the pre-image of a closed set, is itself closed and hence compact. Appealing to Theorem 24.1, (4), we thus obtain that $d(g^{-1}(y)) < \varepsilon$, which is what was to be shown.

Chapter 8

METRIZATION OF TOPOLOGICAL SPACES

§ 26. The Principal Theorems

We have already established in § 2 that every metric on a set $\mathfrak{X}$ induces a topology on $\mathfrak{X}$—and further that quite different metrics on $\mathfrak{X}$ can induce the same topology on $\mathfrak{X}$. Conversely, however, not every topology $\mathfrak{T}$ on a set $\mathfrak{X}$ is metrizable (cf. Definition 2.3), i.e. not every topology is induced by a metric. In this chapter, we shall deal with the question of which topologies $\mathfrak{T}$ are metrizable. In any case, the normality of $\mathfrak{T}$ is necessary for the metrizability of $\mathfrak{T}$ (see Theorem 20.6)—furthermore, that every point of $\mathfrak{X}$ possesses a denumerable neighborhood basis is necessary. But these conditions are in general not sufficient. An answer to the metrization problem was first given by P. Urysohn, who proved the following two theorems.

26.1 First Theorem of Urysohn: *A topological space, which is normal and possesses a denumerable basis, is homeomorphic to a subset of a Hilbert space and therefore it is metrizable.*

26.2 Second Theorem of Urysohn: *A compact topological space is metrizable if, and only if, it possesses a denumerable basis.*

In this chapter, we shall prove both these theorems within the framework of the general *metrization theorem.* This theorem, which yields the complete solution of the metrization problem in the form of a necessary and sufficient condition, was discovered—after previous long and vain attempts in this direction had been made—in the years 1950–1951 by Yu. M. Smirnov, J. Nagata and R. H. Bing, independently of one another. In order to be able to formulate it suitably, we first introduce some definitions and auxiliary observations.

26.3 Definition: A system of subsets $\mathfrak{D} = \{D_\lambda \mid \lambda$ from an arbitrary index set $\Lambda\}$ of a topological space $\mathfrak{X}$ is called a *discrete system* of sets if for each $x \in \mathfrak{X}$ there exists a neighborhood U of x which intersects at most one D_λ. A system of subsets $\mathfrak{E} = \{E_\mu \mid \mu$ from an arbitrary index set $M\}$ is called a *locally finite system* of sets if for each $x \in \mathfrak{X}$ there exists a neighborhood U which intersects at most a finite number of the E_μ.

The sets E_μ of the definition are not necessarily meant to be mutually distinct; i.e., we can very well have that $\mu \in M, \mu' \in M, \mu \neq \mu'$, but $E_\mu = E_{\mu'}$. One can also say: To each index $\mu \in M$ there corresponds a subset $E_\mu \subset \mathfrak{X}$ where distinct indices do not necessarily correspond to distinct subsets. Such systems are sometimes called "indexed systems." This remark holds as well for all the systems of sets subsequently discussed.

On the other hand, the sets D_λ in the first part of Definition 26.3 are by definition disjoint. The totality of all one-point subsets of $\mathfrak{X}$ yields an example of a disjoint system which, in general, is neither a discrete, nor a locally finite, system. A discrete system of sets is locally finite, but not conversely. Every subsystem of a discrete system is again discrete; every subsystem of a locally finite system is again locally finite.

26.4 Theorem: *A locally finite system of sets and a fortiori a discrete system of sets of a compact space* $\mathfrak{X}$ *is finite.*

Proof: For each $x \in \mathfrak{X}$ there exists a neighborhood U_x of x which intersects only a finite number of the E_μ (in the notation of Definition 26.3). A finite number of the U_x cover $\mathfrak{X}$ and therefore there are only a finite number of the E_μ.

26.5 Theorem: *For a locally finite system (in the notation of Definition* 26.3),

$$\overline{\bigcup E_\mu} = \bigcup \overline{E}_\mu$$

holds.

Proof: According to Theorem 3.5, we have that $\overline{\bigcup E_\mu} \supset \bigcup \overline{E}_\mu$ trivially. In order to prove the reverse inclusion, let us take an $x \in \overline{\bigcup E_\mu}$ and a neighborhood U_x of x which intersects only a finite number of the E_μ, say $E_0, \ldots, E_r$. Then $x \in \overline{E_0 \cup \ldots \cup E_r}$ must obviously hold. It thus follows (see Theorem 3.6) that

$$x \in \overline{E_0 \cup \ldots \cup E_r} = \overline{E}_0 \cup \ldots \cup \overline{E}_r \subset \bigcup \overline{E}_\mu.$$

26.6 Definition: A system of sets $\mathfrak{D}$ is called *σ-discrete* if it is the union of a denumerable number of discrete systems $\mathfrak{D}_n$ ($n = 1, 2, \ldots$). A system of sets $\mathfrak{E}$ is called *σ-locally finite* if it is the union of a denumerable number of locally finite systems $\mathfrak{E}_n (n = 1, 2, \ldots)$.

We write σ-discrete and the corresponding σ-locally finite systems and their sets in the form

$$\mathfrak{D} = \bigcup_{n=1}^{\infty} \mathfrak{D}_n = \bigcup_{n=1}^{\infty} \{D_{n\lambda} \mid \lambda \in \Lambda\} = \{D_{n\lambda} \mid n = 1, 2, \ldots; \lambda \in \Lambda\}.$$

Here, the index set Λ should really have been denoted by Λ_n and the indices λ really as λ_n; but, for the sake of brevity, we omit the index n by taking a correspondingly larger index set Λ, say the union of such Λ_n, and assuming a corresponding number of empty sets for the $D_{n\lambda}$.

We can now formulate the next theorem.

26.7 Metrization Theorem: *An arbitrary topological space $\mathfrak{X}$ is metrizable if, and only if, it satisfies any one of the following two equivalent conditions:*

[*Mb*] *$\mathfrak{X}$ is regular and possesses a σ-discrete basis.*

[*Mb'*] *$\mathfrak{X}$ is regular and possesses a σ-locally finite basis.*

The condition [*Mb'*] is due to Smirnov and Nagata; [*Mb*] is due to Bing. It appears to be astonishing that such a straightforward condition governs the metrizability of an arbitrary topological space. Moreover, in both conditions, the word "regular" can be relaced by "normal" as the following proofs show; then [*Mb*] and [*Mb'*], respectively, assert formally somewhat more as a necessary condition and somewhat less as a sufficient condition. We note that the conditions [*Mb*] and [*Mb'*] hold exactly the middle road between the condition of denumerable neighborhood bases which is well-known to be a necessary condition and the sufficient condition of denumerable bases in the first Urysohn Theorem.

We shall first prove that the Urysohn theorems follow from the metrization theorem. If $\mathfrak{X}$ is normal with denumerable basis $\mathfrak{B}$, then $\mathfrak{X}$ is also regular and $\mathfrak{B}$ is σ-discrete. Therefore, according to the metrization theorem, $\mathfrak{X}$ is metrizable. This is the first Urysohn Theorem; a later proof (see § 28) shows that $\mathfrak{X}$ is homeomorphic to a subspace of a Hilbert space.

Now, let $\mathfrak{X}$ be a compact space. Then $\mathfrak{X}$ is normal. If $\mathfrak{X}$ has a denumerable, hence a σ-discrete, basis, then according to the metrization theorem $\mathfrak{X}$ is metrizable. Conversely, if the space $\mathfrak{X}$ is metrizable, then $\mathfrak{X}$ is normal and according to the metrization theorem it possesses a σ-discrete basis. According to Theorem 26.4, this σ-discrete basis is a denumerable union of finite systems and hence it is itself denumerable. This is the second Urysohn Theorem.

We shall prove in § 27 that [*Mb*] is necessary for metrizability and in § 28 that [*Mb'*] is sufficient for metrizability. Since [*Mb'*] is a consequence of [*Mb*], this will complete the proof of the metrization theorem.

§ 27. Necessary Conditions

We have to show that a metric space satisfies the condition [*Mb*]. As we shall see, this will be yielded essentially by the following theorem which was first proved by A. H. Stone.

27.1 Theorem: *Every open covering* $\mathfrak{D}$ *of a metric space* $\mathfrak{X}$ *possesss an open* σ*-discrete refinement.*

A Hausdorff topological space which possesses the property which is stated in this theorem for metric spaces is called *paracompact*. This concept, which is important in many modern investigations, is used only implicitly within the framework of this little volume.

Proof: Let $\mathfrak{D} = \{D_\lambda \mid \lambda \in \Lambda\}$ be a given open covering. We assume the index set Λ to be well-ordered (cf. E. KAMKE [1], § 41) so that for each pair of indices $\mu, \nu \in \Lambda$ it is determined whether $\mu = \nu, \mu > \nu$, $\mu < \nu$ and that every non-empty subset of Λ has a first element; 0 is the first element of Λ. Let n denote a natural number 1, 2, . . . which is first of all chosen fixed. We then define, by transfinite induction (see E. KAMKE [1], § 36),

$$A_{n0} = \mathcal{A}_{\frac{1}{2^n}}(D_0), A_{n\nu} = \mathcal{A}_{\frac{1}{2^n}}(D_\nu - \bigcup_{\nu'<\nu} A_{n\nu'}).$$

Then $A_{n\nu} \subset D_\nu$ and even every $\frac{1}{2^n}$ -open-neighborhood of a point in $A_{n\nu}$ is contained in D_ν. Further, we have that $d(A_{n\nu}, A_{n\mu}) \geqq \frac{1}{2^n}$ provided $\nu \neq \mu$ and both sets are $\neq \emptyset$. Namely, if say $\mu < \nu$, then $A_{n\mu}$ is contained in the complementary set $\complement B$ of $B = D_\nu - \bigcup A_{n\nu'}$ and the asserted inequality follows from Theorem 20.8. We form further the open sets

$$E_{n\nu} = \mathfrak{U}_{\frac{1}{2^{n+2}}}(A_{n\nu}),$$

which are likewise contained in D_ν, and assert that the system of sets $\mathfrak{E}_n = \{E_{n\nu}\}$ is discrete (always with fixed n). Namely, let p be an arbitrary point in $\mathfrak{X}$. We assert, more specifically, that the $\frac{1}{2^{n+2}}$-open-neighborhood U of p intersects at most one $E_{n\nu}$. Namely, if we assume that U intersects $E_{n\nu}$ in a point x_ν and $E_{n\mu}$ with $\mu \neq \nu$ in a point x_μ, then we would have that

$$d(p, x_\nu) < \frac{1}{2^{n+2}}, d(p, x_\mu) < \frac{1}{2^{n+2}}.$$

According to the definition of the $E_{n\nu}$, we have that

$$d(x_\nu, y_\nu) < \frac{1}{2^{n+2}}, d(x_\mu, y_\mu) < \frac{1}{2^{n+2}}$$

for suitable point $y_\nu \in A_{n\nu}$ and $y_\mu \in A_{n\mu}$. It would follow from this that $d(y_\nu, y_\mu) < \frac{4}{2^{n+2}} = \frac{1}{2^n}$, contrary to $d(A_{n\nu}, A_{n\mu}) \geqq \frac{1}{2^n}$.

Thus, the system of sets $\mathfrak{E} = \bigcup \mathfrak{E}_n = \{E_{n\nu} \mid n = 1, 2, \ldots; \nu \in \Lambda\}$ is σ-discrete. We shall prove that $\mathfrak{E}$ represents a covering of $\mathfrak{X}$, which will thus prove the theorem. Let p be an arbitrary point in $\mathfrak{X}$ and suppose λ is the smallest index with the property that $p \in D_\lambda$. Then some $\left(\frac{1}{2^n}\right)$-open-neighborhood U of p lies, for suitable n, entirely in D_λ. U has no point in common with $A_{n\lambda'}$ ($\lambda' < \lambda$) for otherwise p would lie in $D_{\lambda'}$. Hence U lies entirely in $D_\lambda - \bigcup A_{n\lambda'}$. Therefore p lies in $A_{n\lambda}$ and consequently in $E_{n\lambda}$, which completes the proof of the theorem.

It is now easy to verify $[Mb]$. Let $\mathfrak{D}_m$, with $m = 1, 2, \ldots$, be the covering of $\mathfrak{X}$ which consists of all $\left(\frac{1}{2^m}\right)$-open-spherical neighborhoods of all points of $\mathfrak{X}$. The sets of $\mathfrak{D}_m$ have diameter $\leqq \frac{1}{2^{m-1}}$. Let the open σ-discrete covering $\mathfrak{E}_m$ be a refinement according to the preceding theorem of the covering $\mathfrak{D}_m$; the diameters of the sets from $\mathfrak{E}_m$ are likewise $\leqq \frac{1}{2^{m-1}}$. $\mathfrak{E} = \bigcup \mathfrak{E}_m$, taken over all $m = 1, 2, \ldots$, is likewise still σ-discrete and we assert that it is a basis of $\mathfrak{X}$. Appealing to the criterion of Theorem 10.2, we choose an open set O and a point $p \in O$ and we have now to prove the existence of a set E in $\mathfrak{E}$ with $p \in E \subset O$. Together with p, a suitable $\left(\frac{1}{2^n}\right)$-open-neighborhood V of p also belongs to O. In the covering $\mathfrak{E}_{n+2}$, p is covered by at least one set $E \in \mathfrak{E}_{n+2}$ of diameter $< \frac{1}{2^n}$. For each point $x \in E$, we have that $d(p, x) \leqq \frac{1}{2^{n+1}} < \frac{1}{2^n}$; therefore, x lies in V. Thus, $p \in E \subset O$, which is what we had to prove. Since a metric space is regular, and even normal, $[Mb]$ is thus completely proved.

§ 28. Sufficient Conditions

In this section, we assume that a topological space $\mathfrak{X}$ satisfies the condition [Mb']. We have to prove the metrizability of $\mathfrak{X}$. The following two lemmas establish first of all the subassertions.

28.1 Lemma: *If a topological space $\mathfrak{X}$ satisfies the condition [Mb'], then every open set in $\mathfrak{X}$ is the union of a denumerable number of closed sets.*

To understand this lemma, the reader should refer to Theorem 20.9.

Proof: Let O be an open subset of $\mathfrak{X}$ and suppose $x \in O$. Because of the regularity condition [Rg''], there exists an open neighborhood V of x with $x \in V \subset \bar{V} \subset O$. We choose an element $E_{n\nu}$ from the σ-locally finite basis $\mathfrak{E}$ of $\mathfrak{X}$ (which exists by [Mb']) such that $x \in E_{n\nu} \subset V$ as is always possible for a basis according to Theorem 10.2. Because $\bar{E}_{n\nu} \subset \bar{V}$, it follows that $x \in \bar{E}_{n\nu} \subset O$. In this way, to each $x \in O$ there corresponds an $E_{n\nu} = E_{n\nu}(x)$, in particular an index $n = n(x)$, such that $x \in \bar{E}_{n\nu}(x) \subset O$. For $k = 1, 2, \ldots$, we form the sets $E_k = \bigcup E_{n\nu}(x)$ taken over those $x \in O$ for which $n(x) = k$. According to Theorem 26.5, we can deduce that

$$\bar{E}_k = \bigcup \bar{E}_{n\nu} \subset O.$$

The $\bar{E}_k$ are closed and contained in O. The union $\bigcup \bar{E}_k$ of all the $\bar{E}_k$ contains all the $x \in O$ and thus is identical with O; this completes the proof of the theorem.

28.2 Lemma: *If the topological space $\mathfrak{X}$ satisfies the condition [Mb'], then $\mathfrak{X}$ is normal.*

Proof: Let A and B be disjoint closed subsets of $\mathfrak{X}$; let x range over the points of A and let y range over the points of B. For each x, we take, as in the preceding proof, a set $E_{n\nu}(x) \in \mathfrak{E}$ with the property that $x \in E_{n\nu}(x) \subset \bar{E}_{n\nu}(x) \subset \complement B$, where the open set O of the preceding proof is to be identified with $\complement B$. For A and correspondingly for B we form

$$F_k = \cup E_{n\nu}(x) \text{ over all } x \in A \text{ with } n(x) = k,$$

$$G_l = \cup E_{n\nu}(y) \text{ over all } y \in B \text{ with } n(y) = l.$$

Both of these sets are open and we have that $\bar{F}_k = \cup \bar{E}_{n\nu}(x) \subset \complement B$ (see Theorem 26.5); therefore, $\bar{F}_k \cap B = \emptyset$. It follows in exactly the same way that $\bar{G}_l \cap A = \emptyset$.

Further, we form

$$U_k = F_k - \cup \bar{G}_l \text{ over all } l \leqq k;$$

$$V_l = G_l - \cup \bar{F}_k \text{ over all } k \leqq l.$$

These sets are also open. U_k contains all x with $n(x) = k$ and V_l contains all y with $n(y) = l$. Finally, we form

$$U = \cup U_k \text{ with } k = 1, 2, \ldots; \; V = \cup V_l \text{ with } l = 1, 2, \ldots.$$

U is open and contains all $x \in A$, i.e. U contains A; thus, U is a neighborhood of A and V is a neighborhood of B. Further, $U_k \cap V_l = \emptyset$; for $l \leqq k$, this follows from the definition of U_k and for $k \leqq l$ it follows from the definition of V_l. From this it follows that $U \cap V = \emptyset$ which shows the normality of $\mathfrak{X}$.

We now arrive at the metrization proper of $\mathfrak{X}$. As before, we assume that $\mathfrak{X}$ satisfies the condition [Mb'] and accordingly possesses a σ-locally finite basis

$$\mathfrak{E} = \cup \mathfrak{E}_n = \{E_{n\nu} \mid n = 1, 2, \ldots; \nu \in \Lambda\}$$

which consists of the locally finite systems $\mathfrak{E}_n$. Moreover, we can assume according to the last theorem that $\mathfrak{X}$ is normal.

Each of the open sets $E_{n\nu}$ is, according to Theorem 28.1, the union of a denumerable number of closed sets. Thus, we can apply the Urysohn Theorem 15.3 to each set $E_{n\nu}$: For each $E_{n\nu}$ there exists a continuous real-valued function $\varphi_{n\nu}$ with $0 \leqq \varphi_{n\nu}(x) \leqq 1$ for which $\varphi_{n\nu}(x) > 0$ if, and only if, $x \in E_{n\nu}$. For each fixed x, we set

$$\psi_{n\nu}(x) = \frac{\varphi_{n\nu}(x)}{\sqrt{1 + \sum \varphi^2_{n\nu'}(x)}},$$

summed over all $\nu' \in \Lambda$. Since for fixed n a point x lies in only a finite number of the $E_{n\nu'}$, the sum under the radical is finite. The function $\psi_{n\nu}(x)$ has the following properties:

(1) $0 \leqq \psi_{n\nu}(x) \leqq 1$; $\psi_{n\nu}(x) \neq 0$ if, and only if, $x \in E_{n\nu}$;

(2) for fixed n and fixed x, only a finite number of $\psi_{n\nu}(x)$ are $\neq 0$;

(3) for fixed n, $\sum \psi^2_{n\nu}(x) < 1$, $\sum(\psi_{n\nu}(x) - \psi_{n\nu}(y))^2 < 2$, where both sums range over all $\nu \in \Lambda$.

(3) follows from the definition of $\psi_{n\nu}(x)$ and by deleting the parentheses in the well-known way.

We now form a generalized Hilbert space H using the set of all index pairs (n, ν). Let a point p of H be a system of real numbers $p_{n\nu}$, one for each index pair (n, ν), which are called the coordinates of p; suppose that only a denumerable number of the coordinates of a point p are $\neq 0$ and that the sum $\sum p^2_{n\nu}$ over all coordinates of p is convergent. H becomes a metric space by the definition

$$d(p, q) = \sqrt{\sum_{n,\nu}(q_{n\nu} - p_{n\nu})^2},$$

summed over all index pairs (n, ν). One verifies that the sum is finite, that $d(p, q)$ is therefore well-defined, and that the axioms [M 1]–[M 3] hold exactly as is the case in ordinary Hilbert space (§ 1, example (b)). This reduces to a special case for our present construction if Λ consists of only one element.

We define a mapping $f: \mathfrak{X} \to H$ by assigning to the point $x \in \mathfrak{X}$ the point $p = f(x) \in H$ whose coordinates are given by

$$p_{n\nu}(x) = \frac{1}{\sqrt{2^n}}\psi_{n\nu}(x).$$

In fact, for each x, according to (2), only a finite number of the $p_{n\nu}(x)$ are $\neq 0$ and the sum $\sum p^2_{n\nu} = \sum_n \left(\frac{1}{2^n}\right) \cdot \sum_\nu \psi^2_{n\nu}(x)$ is, according to (3), smaller than $\sum\left(\frac{1}{2^n}\right) = 1$ and converges so that in this way a point $p = f(x)$ of H is actually determined. Concerning f, we now prove: (α) f is a monomorphism; (β) f is continuous; (γ) f^{-1} is continuous. This then exhibits f as a homeomorphic mapping of $\mathfrak{X}$ into a subset of H and the metric of H evidently induces a metric in $\mathfrak{X}$, as we wished to construct.

(α): If x, y, $x \neq y$, are two points of $\mathfrak{X}$, then there exists a neighborhood of x which does not contain y and thus there exists a set $E_{n\nu}$ which contains x but not y. Then $\varphi_{n\nu}(x) \neq 0$ but $\varphi_{n\nu}(y) = 0$ and $p_{n\nu}(x) > 0$ but $p_{n\nu}(y) = 0$. Therefore, $p = f(x)$ and $q = f(y)$ differ in these coordinates and are thus distinct points of H. It is thus shown that f is a monomorphism.

(β): Let $x \in \mathfrak{X}$ and $\varepsilon > 0$ be given. We must find a $W \in \mathfrak{U}(x)$ with the property that

$$\{d(f(x), f(y))\}^2 = \sum_{n,\nu}(p_{n\nu}(y) - p_{n\nu}(x))^2 < \varepsilon^2$$

provided $y \in W$.

For every natural number N,

$$\sum_{n>N,\nu} (p_{n\nu}(y) - p_{n\nu}(x))^2 = \sum_{n>N} \frac{1}{2^n} \sum_{\nu} (\psi_{n\nu}(y) - \psi_{n\nu}(x))^2$$

$$\leqq \sum_{n>N} \frac{1}{2^n} \cdot 2 = \frac{2}{2^N}$$

holds. The sum becomes $< \dfrac{\varepsilon^2}{2}$ when $2^N > \dfrac{4}{\varepsilon^2}$. We choose N so that this is the case.

Because of the local-finiteness of $\mathfrak{E}_n$, for every fixed n, there exists a neighborhood U_x of x which intersects only a finite number of the $E_{n\nu}$. If n ranges over the finite number of natural numbers $\leqq N$, then also only a finite number of the $E_{n\nu}$ meet the intersection neighborhood $U = \bigcap U_n$. For the moment, this finite number of $E_{n\nu}$ can be called the essential $E_{n\nu}$ and let the number of them be s. The corresponding s "essential" functions $p_{n\nu}(x)$ are continuous in x so that one can find neighborhoods $V_{n\nu}$ of x such that for these $p_{n\nu}(x)$,

$$| p_{n\nu}(y) - p_{n\nu}(x) | < \frac{\varepsilon}{\sqrt{2s}} \text{ provided } y \in V_{n\nu}.$$

For the non-essential $p_{n\nu}$ with $n \leqq N$, we have, according to the definition of U, that $p_{n\nu}(x) = 0$ as well as $p_{n\nu}(y) = 0$ when $y \in U$, so that for these $p_{n\nu}$, $| p_{n\nu}(y) - p_{n\nu}(x) | = 0$ holds, if we restrict y to U. If we form the intersection neighborhood $W = (\bigcap V_{n\nu}) \cap U$, where only a finite number of "essential" $V_{n\nu}$ are meant, then, combining all essential and non-essential $p_{n\nu}$ with $n < N$ and arbitrary ν, we can conclude that: If $x \in W$, then

$$\sum_{n \leqq N, \nu} (p_{n\nu}(y) - p_{n\nu}(x))^2 < s \cdot \frac{\varepsilon^2}{2s} = \frac{\varepsilon^2}{2}$$

holds. The desired result follows from this formula together with the end formula of the first subsection under (β) by addition.

(γ) f^{-1} maps $f(\mathfrak{X})$ monomorphically onto $\mathfrak{X}$. If again $x = f^{-1}(p)$, then we have to show that: For each neighborhood $U \in \mathfrak{U}(x)$ there exists a $\delta = \delta(U)$ such that $y = f^{-1}(q) \in U$ provided $d(q, p) < \delta$. Hence, let U be given. There exists an $E_{n_0\nu_0}$ with $x \in E_{n_0\nu_0} \subset U$. We shall show that is suffices to set $\delta = p_{n_0\nu_0}(x)$. Namely we have that

$$| p_{n_0\nu_0}(y) - p_{n_0\nu_0}(x) | \leqq \sqrt{\sum_{n,\nu} (p_{n\nu}(y) - p_{n\nu}(x))^2} = d(p, q).$$

But it follows from $| p_{n_0\nu_0}(y) - p_{n_0\nu_0}(x) | < p_{n_0\nu_0}(x)$ that $p_{n_0\nu_0}(y) \neq 0$ and therefore that $y \in E_{n_0\nu_0} \subset U$, which is what we had to prove. We have thus shown that $\mathfrak{X}$ can be embedded homeomorphically in H and hence the metrization theorem is completely proved.

Part IV

RUDIMENTS OF DIMENSION THEORY

Chapter 9

POLYHEDRA

§ 29. Simplexes

We shall now study a very much more special class of spaces—the so-called polyhedra. They serve first of all in the next chapter to build up dimension theory. Later, they will form the foundation for algebraic topology. Polyhedra will be defined in an altogether different way than the spaces studied up to this point. Namely, we combine them from simple, perfectly obvious building blocks. This occurs within an N-dimensional Euclidean space R^N. Accordingly, we discuss first the simplest properties of R^N, but we must assume a certain familiarity with the fundamental geometric and algebraic facts—since we must start at some definite point in order to make progress. Still some basic material is needed in order that our subsequent discussion be as clear as possible.

1. We denote the points of R^N by small German letters which simultaneously mean the corresponding position vectors, $\mathfrak{x} = (x_1, \ldots, x_N)$. The *unit points* $\mathfrak{e}_i$ $(i = 1, \ldots, N)$ have i-th coordinate equal to 1 whereas all the other coordinates are zero. We say that the $n + 1$ points $\mathfrak{p}_0, \ldots,$ $\mathfrak{p}_n$ $(n \geqq 1)$ are *independent* if the n vectors $\mathfrak{p}_1 - \mathfrak{p}_0, \ldots, \mathfrak{p}_n - \mathfrak{p}_0$ are linearly independent; furthermore, a single point $\mathfrak{p}_0$ is said to be independent. For example, the zero point 0 and $\mathfrak{e}_1, \ldots, \mathfrak{e}_N$ are independent. The maximal number of independent points in R^N is $N + 1$.

Every non-empty subsystem of an independent system of points is again independent. The considerations of the following subsection 3 show that the definition of independence is symmetric in the $n + 1$ points $\mathfrak{p}_0, \ldots, \mathfrak{p}_n$.

2. First of all, let $\mathfrak{p}_0, \ldots, \mathfrak{p}_n$ be arbitrary points in R^N. The set of points $\mathfrak{x}$ of the form

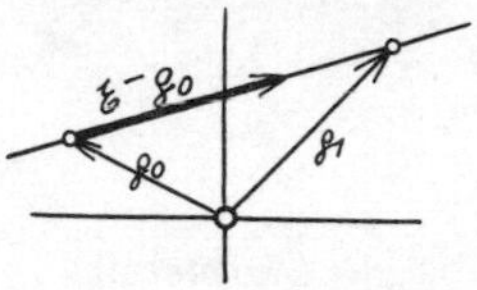

Fig. 5

$$\mathfrak{x} = \mathfrak{p}_0 + \mu_1 (\mathfrak{p}_1 - \mathfrak{p}_0) + \ldots + \mu_n(\mathfrak{p}_n - \mathfrak{p}_0),$$

with arbitrary real $\mu_1, \ldots, \mu_n$, is called the (linear) *subspace* spanned by $\mathfrak{p}_0, \ldots, \mathfrak{p}_n$ (see Fig. 5). These points can also be written in the form

$$\mathfrak{x} = (1 - \sum_{j=1}^{n} \mu_j)\mathfrak{p}_0 + \mu_1\mathfrak{p}_1 + \ldots + \mu_n\mathfrak{p}_n$$

$$= \sum_{i=0}^{n} \lambda_i\mathfrak{p}_i \text{ with} \sum_{i=0}^{n} \lambda_i = 1.$$

Here, as in the sequel, we sum over i from 0 to n whereas over j from 1 to n.

Also, conversely, every point $\mathfrak{x} = \sum_{i=0}^{n} \lambda_i\mathfrak{p}_i$ with $\sum_{i=0}^{n} \lambda_i = 1$ belongs to the subspace thus spanned since

$$\mathfrak{x} = \sum_{i=0}^{n} \lambda_i\mathfrak{p}_i = \mathfrak{p}_0 + \lambda_1(\mathfrak{p}_1 - \mathfrak{p}_0) + \ldots + \lambda_n(\mathfrak{p}_n - \mathfrak{p}_0).$$

3. The following theorem holds: $\mathfrak{p}_0, \ldots, \mathfrak{p}_n$ are independent if, and only if, the representation $\mathfrak{x} = \sum\lambda_i\mathfrak{p}_i$ with $\sum\lambda_i = 1$ of the points of the spanned subspace is unique. That is, if these points are independent, then it follows from

$$\mathfrak{x} = \sum_{i=0}^{n} \lambda_i\mathfrak{p}_i = \sum_{i=0}^{n} \mu_i\mathfrak{p}_i \text{ with} \sum_{i=0}^{n} \lambda_i = \sum_{i=0}^{n} \mu_i = 1$$

that

$$\sum(\lambda_i - \mu_i)\mathfrak{p}_i = 0, \sum(\lambda_i - \mu_i)\mathfrak{p}_0 = 0, \sum(\lambda_i - \mu_i)\,(\mathfrak{p}_i - \mathfrak{p}_0) = 0$$

and therefore $\lambda_j = \mu_j$ for $j = 1, \ldots, n$ and then also $\lambda_0 = \mu_0$.

Conversely, if this representation is unique, then it follows from $\sum\alpha_j(\mathfrak{p}_j - \mathfrak{p}_0) = 0$ that

$$\sum_{j=1}^{n} \alpha_j\mathfrak{p}_j - \sum_{j=1}^{n} \alpha_j\mathfrak{p}_0 = 0; (1 - \sum_{j=1}^{n} \alpha_j)\,\mathfrak{p}_0 + \sum_{j=1}^{n} \alpha_j\,\mathfrak{p}_j = \mathfrak{p}_0.$$

Here, the sum of the coefficients equals 1; because of the uniqueness of the representation we therefore have that $\alpha_j = 0$ for $j = 1, \ldots, n$, i.e. the $\mathfrak{p}_0, \ldots, \mathfrak{p}_n$ are independent. For $n = 1$, we obtain the *line joining* $\mathfrak{p}_0$ and $\mathfrak{p}_1$, i.e. the set of points $\mathfrak{x} = \lambda\mathfrak{p}_0 + (1 - \lambda)\mathfrak{p}_1$; $(1 - \lambda) : \lambda$ denotes the *division ratio* into which the segment $(\mathfrak{p}_0\mathfrak{p}_1)$ is divided by $\mathfrak{x}$.

4. We say that the subspace spanned by the $n + 1$ independent points $\mathfrak{p}_i$ $(i = 0, \ldots, n)$ has the *(algebraic) dimension n*. If one chooses the fixed independent points $\mathfrak{p}_i$ as the spanning points, then, according to what we have already proved, the representation $\mathfrak{x} = \sum\lambda_i\mathfrak{p}_i$ with $\sum\lambda_i = 1$ (summed from $i = 0$ to $i = n$) of the points of the subspace is unique. Therefore, the λ_i can be considered to be the coordinates of the points $\mathfrak{x}$ of the subspace. They are called the *barycentric coordinates* of the subspace with the reference points $\mathfrak{p}_0, \ldots, \mathfrak{p}_n$. This nomenclature goes back to an interpretation in mechanics: Imagine masses with a total sum of 1 distributed at the points $\mathfrak{p}_i$; then $\mathfrak{x}$ is the center of gravity of these masses. In this interpretation, the uniqueness of the λ_i also appears plausible; one has naturally to allow negative masses. The spanning points $\mathfrak{p}_i$ have the coordinates of the unit vectors $(0, \ldots, 0, 1, 0, \ldots, 0)$ as barycentric coordinates. If one takes the unit vectors $\mathfrak{e}_i$ as spanning vectors of an $(N - 1)$–dimensional subspace, the so-called *unit hyperplane*, then there the barycentric coordinates coincide with the ordinary cartesian coordinates.

5. Let m points $\mathfrak{x}_k$ $(k = 1, \ldots, m)$,

$$\mathfrak{x}_k = \sum_{i=0}^{n} \lambda_{ki}\,\mathfrak{p}_i \text{ with } \sum_{i=0}^{n} \lambda_{ki} = 1$$

be given in the subspace spanned by the independent points $\mathfrak{p}_i$ $(i = 0, \ldots, n)$.

We assert: These m points $\mathfrak{x}_k$ are independent if, and only if, the coefficient matrix (λ_{ki}) has the rank m. In fact, the $\mathfrak{x}_k$ are independent if, and only if, the representation of the points $\mathfrak{z} = \sum\mu_k\mathfrak{x}_k$ with $\sum\mu_k = 1$ (summed from $k = 1$ to $k = m$) spanned by them is unique. Now,

$$\mathfrak{z} = \sum_{k=1}^{m} \mu_k\mathfrak{x}_k = \sum_{i=0}^{n}\Big(\sum_{k=1}^{m} \mu_k\lambda_{ki}\Big)\mathfrak{p}_i = \sum_{i=0}^{n} \bar{\lambda}_i\mathfrak{p}_i \text{ with } \sum_{i=0}^{n} \bar{\lambda}_i = 1$$

and the $\bar{\lambda}_i$ are uniquely determined by $\mathfrak{z}$; this yields $n + 1$ equations

$$\bar{\lambda}_i = \sum_{k=1}^{m} \mu_k\lambda_{ki},\; i = 0, \ldots, n$$

for the m "unknowns" μ_k, and the solution is unique if, and only if, the rank of the coefficient matrix is m. Thus, $n + 1$ is the maximal number of independent points in the subspace spanned by $\mathfrak{p}_0, \ldots, \mathfrak{p}_n$.

29.1 Definition: Let $\mathfrak{p}_0, \ldots, \mathfrak{p}_n$ be independent points of the Euclidean space R^N. The set of all points $\mathfrak{x}$ of the form $\mathfrak{x} = \sum\lambda_i\mathfrak{p}_i$ with $\sum\lambda_i = 1$ (summed over $i = 0, \ldots, n$) and $\lambda_i > 0$ is called the *open n-dimensional simplex* $(\sigma) = (\sigma^n) = (\mathfrak{p}_0 \ldots \mathfrak{p}_n)$ with the vertices $\mathfrak{p}_0, \ldots, \mathfrak{p}_n$. If one demands instead of $\lambda_i > 0$ only that $\lambda_i \geqq 0$, then the corresponding set is called the *closed n-dimensional simplex* $[\sigma] = [\sigma^n] = [\mathfrak{p}_0 \ldots \mathfrak{p}_n]$. By simply the *n-dimensional simplex* $\sigma = \sigma^n = \mathfrak{p}_0 \ldots \mathfrak{p}_n$ we understand the open or closed simplex. The set $\dot{\sigma}^n = [\sigma^n] - (\sigma^n)$ is called the *boundary* of the simplex σ^n. For $\dot{\sigma}^1$, we write $\dot{\sigma}$.

The "dimension" n of the n-simplex σ^n will, to distinguish it from geometric dimension to be introduced in the next chapter, also be called the *algebraic dimension* of σ^n.

For $n = 0$, the n-simplex is a point; for $n = 1$ it is an open interval (a, b) or a closed interval $[a, b]$; for $n = 2$ it is a triangle (including the inside of the triangle); for $n = 3$ a tetrahedron. σ^n can be thought of as the simplest n-dimensional figure in the geometry of the space R^N.

We have that $[\sigma^0] = (\sigma^0)$ and therefore the boundary of $\sigma^0 = \emptyset$, as one can verify directly on the basis of the definition.

$[\sigma^n]$ is a closed and bounded point set in R^N and hence it is a compact point set in R^N. (σ^n) is in general not open in R^N, but it is however open in the embedded n-dimensional subspace. The $(N - 1)$-dimensional simplex, with the vertices $\mathfrak{e}_1, \ldots, \mathfrak{e}_N$, situated in the unit hyperplane is called the *unit simplex* of R^N.

$[\sigma]$ and (σ) are convex point sets of R^N. Namely, if $\mathfrak{x}_1 = \sum\lambda_{1i}\mathfrak{p}_i$ and $\mathfrak{x}_2 = \sum\lambda_{2i}\mathfrak{p}_i$ with $\sum\lambda_{1i} = \sum\lambda_{2i} = 1$, summed over $i = 0, \ldots, n$, $\lambda_{1i} \geqq 0$, $\lambda_{2i} \geqq 0$ are points from $[\sigma]$ and if $\mathfrak{x}$ is a point on the segment $[\mathfrak{x}_1\mathfrak{x}_2]$ joining $\mathfrak{x}_1$ and $\mathfrak{x}_2$, $\mathfrak{x} = \mu\mathfrak{x}_1 + (1 - \mu)\mathfrak{x}_2$ with $0 \leqq \mu \leqq 1$, then

$$\mathfrak{x} = \sum_{i=0}^{n} (\mu\lambda_{1i} + (1 - \mu)\lambda_{2i})\mathfrak{p}_i,$$

where the sum of the coefficients is again equal to 1 and the individual coefficients are not negative; therefore, $\mathfrak{x}$ likewise lies in $[\sigma]$.

One shows the convexity of (σ) in a similar way. Moreover, $[\sigma]$ is the convex hull of the spanning points $\mathfrak{p}_0, \ldots, \mathfrak{p}_n$.

The r-dimensional simplexes which are spanned by arbitrary $r + 1$ of the $n + 1$ vertices of σ are called the r-dimensional *face simplexes*—briefly, the *faces* σ^r of $\sigma = \sigma^n$. The points of σ^r are characterized by the fact that those barycentric coordinates which correspond to the vertices which are not involved in σ^r vanish. The number of all r-dimensional faces of σ equals $\binom{n+1}{r+1}$. For $r = 0$, these are the $n + 1$ vertices of σ, for $r = 1$, the $\binom{n+1}{2}$ edges. σ itself is considered to be an improper face of σ; the lower-dimensional faces of σ are called the proper faces. In case r is $< n$, we say that σ^r is *incident* with $\sigma = \sigma^n$ and we write $\sigma^r \prec \sigma^n$.

The faces $[\sigma^r]$ of σ are subsets of $[\sigma]$. *The totality of all open face simplexes of σ, including σ itself, forms a partition of* $[\sigma]$.

For each r-dimensional face simplex σ^r with $0 \leqq r \leqq n - 1$ of σ, there exists an opposite $(n - r - 1)$-dimensional face simplex σ^{n-r-1}, which is spanned by the $(n + 1) - (r + 1) = n - r$ vertices of σ which are not involved in σ^r. σ^{n-r-1} is also called the simplex opposite to σ^r. Only σ itself has no opposite simplex.

29.2 Theorem: *The diameter of an n-simplex σ^n is equal to the length l of its longest edge.*

Proof: If $\mathfrak{x}$ and $\mathfrak{y}$ are two points of σ and if, for instance, $\mathfrak{p}_0$ is one of the vertices of σ which is the farthest removed from $\mathfrak{x}$, then the length $d(\mathfrak{x}, \mathfrak{y})$ of the segment $[\mathfrak{x}, \mathfrak{y}]$ is at most equal to the length $d(\mathfrak{x}, \mathfrak{p}_0)$ of the segment $[\mathfrak{x}, \mathfrak{p}_0]$. For, the closed sphere with center $\mathfrak{x}$ and with the radius $d(\mathfrak{x}, \mathfrak{p}_0)$ contains all the vertices $\mathfrak{p}_0, \ldots, \mathfrak{p}_n$ of σ and hence all of σ and, in particular, $\mathfrak{y}$ also. If, say, $\mathfrak{p}_1$ is one of the vertices of σ which is the farthest removed from $\mathfrak{p}_0$, then $d(\mathfrak{x}, \mathfrak{p}_0) \leqq d(\mathfrak{p}_0, \mathfrak{p}_1)$ for the same reason. The assertion now follows from $d(\mathfrak{x}, \mathfrak{y}) \leqq d(\mathfrak{x}, \mathfrak{p}_0) \leqq d(\mathfrak{p}_0, \mathfrak{p}_1) \leqq l$.

29.3 Theorem: $(\sigma) = (\mathfrak{p}_0 \ldots \mathfrak{p}_n)$ *with* $n \geqq 1$ *consists of all points* $\mathfrak{x}$ *of the open interval* $(\mathfrak{p}_0, \mathfrak{z})$ *with arbitrary* $\mathfrak{z}$ *from* $(\mathfrak{p}_1 \ldots \mathfrak{p}_n)$.

Proof: Let $\mathfrak{x} \in (\sigma)$ with the representation $\mathfrak{x} = \sum \lambda_i \mathfrak{p}_i$, $\sum \lambda_i = 1$, $\lambda_i > 0$ summed over $i = 0, \ldots, n$. If we set

$$\sum_{j=1}^{n} \lambda_j = \lambda \text{ and hence } \lambda_0 + \lambda = 1, \sum_{j=1}^{n} \frac{\lambda_j}{\lambda} = 1,$$

then it follows that

$$\mathfrak{x} = \lambda_0 \mathfrak{p}_0 + \sum_{j=1}^{n} \lambda_j \mathfrak{p}_j = \lambda_0 \mathfrak{p}_0 + \lambda \sum_{j=1}^{n} \frac{\lambda_j}{\lambda} \mathfrak{p}_j = \lambda_0 \mathfrak{p}_0 + \lambda \mathfrak{z}$$

with $\mathfrak{z} \in (\mathfrak{p}_1 \ldots \mathfrak{p}_n)$. This representation $\mathfrak{x} = \lambda_0 \mathfrak{p}_0 + \lambda \mathfrak{z}$ with $\lambda_0 + \lambda = 1$ is obviously unique.

The set (σ) and likewise the set $[\sigma]$ determines the vertices $\mathfrak{p}_i$ $(i = 0, \ldots, n)$ uniquely. Since $[\sigma]$ is the closure of (σ), if suffices to show this for $[\sigma]$. This will be accomplished by the following assertion: Every point $\mathfrak{x} \neq \mathfrak{p}_i$ of $[\sigma]$ is the midpoint of a suitable segment $[\mathfrak{y}\mathfrak{z}]$ with $\mathfrak{y}, \mathfrak{z} \in [\sigma]$, $\mathfrak{y} \neq \mathfrak{z}$; however, this does not hold for the $\mathfrak{p}_i$. We give an indication of the proof: For the $\mathfrak{x} \neq \mathfrak{p}_i$, the assertion follows from the last theorem since every such point $\mathfrak{x}$ belongs to an open face simplex of σ of dimension $\geqq 1$. We easily recognize that a vertex $\mathfrak{p}_i$ cannot be the midpoint of a segment $[\mathfrak{y}, \mathfrak{z}]$, i.e. we cannot have $\mathfrak{p}_i = \frac{1}{2}(\mathfrak{y} + \mathfrak{z})$, if we write this equation in barycentric coordinates.

§ 30. Simplicial Complexes and Polyhedra

30.1 Definition: A set K of a finite number of simplexes in a Euclidean space R^N is called a *simplicial complex*—briefly a *complex*—if the following two conditions are satisfied:

[*S* 1] Together with every simplex, each of its faces also occurs in K.

[*S* 2] If σ_1 and σ_2 are two distinct simplexes of K, then $(\sigma_1) \cap (\sigma_2) = \emptyset$.

The largest of the (algebraic) dimensions of the simplexes of K is called the (*algebraic*) *dimension* of K. A subset Λ of a complex K is called a *subcomplex* of K if Λ is a simplicial complex, i.e. the condition [*S* 1] of Definition 30.1 is satisfied; the condition [*S* 2] holds in this case automatically.

For every integer $q \geqq 0$, the simplexes of a complex K having dimension at most q obviously form a subcomplex; it is called the *q-dimensional skeleton* K_q of K. If σ_1 and σ_2 are two distinct simplexes of K, which have the vertices $\mathfrak{p}_0, \ldots, \mathfrak{p}_r$, and only these, in common, then we surely have that $[\sigma_1] \cap [\sigma_2] \supset [\mathfrak{p}_0 \ldots \mathfrak{p}_r]$. Any common point $\mathfrak{x}$ of $[\sigma_1]$ and $[\sigma_2]$ lies in a well-defined open face simplex (σ_1') of σ_1 and in a well-defined open face simplex (σ_2') of σ_2. The condition $[S\ 2]$ then asserts that $\sigma_1' = \sigma_2'$. The simplex is then a face of $[\mathfrak{p}_0 \ldots \mathfrak{p}_r]$. Therefore the following assertion holds:

$[S\ 2']$ If σ_1 and σ_2 are two distinct simplexes of K, then $[\sigma_1] \cap [\sigma_2]$ is empty or a common closed face simplex of σ_1 and σ_2.

Since, as we have seen, not only is $[S\ 2']$ a consequence of $[S\ 2]$, but also, obviously, $[S\ 2]$ is a consequence of $[S\ 2']$, and the condition $[S\ 2']$ is equivalent to the condition $[S\ 2]$ in Definition 30.1.

Examples: (1) The totality of all the faces of a simplex $\sigma = \sigma^n$, including σ itself, forms an n-dimensional complex T^n.

(2) The totality of all the proper faces of a simplex $\sigma = \sigma^{n+1}$ form an n-dimensional complex $\sum^n$.

A further example of a 2-dimensional complex is sketched in Fig. 6.

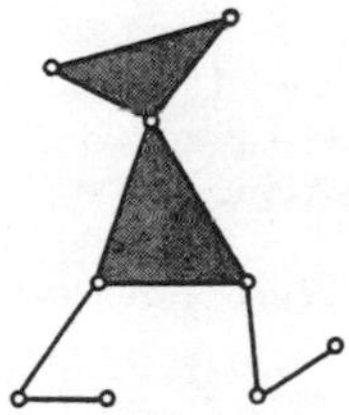

Fig. 6

30.2 Definition: Two simplicial complexes K_1 and K_2 are said to be *isomorphic*—in symbols, $\mathsf{K}_1 \approx \mathsf{K}_2$—if the simplexes of K_1 and K_2 correspond, in every dimension $q = 0, 1, 2, \ldots$, in one-to-one fashion such that incident simplexes always correspond to incident simplexes. One also says that K_2 is a *realization* of K_1.

Every simplicial complex K admits two distinguished realizations:

I. *Unit realization.* We correspond to the vertices $\mathfrak{p}_i$ ($i = 1, \ldots, \alpha_0$) of K the unit points $\mathfrak{e}_i$ in the Euclidean space R^{α_0}; to a simplex of K, which is spanned by certain of the vertices $\mathfrak{p}_i$, we correspond the simplex in R^{α_0} which is spanned by the corresponding vertices.

It is clear that we obtain as the image K′ of K a simplicial complex K′, and indeed a subcomplex of the unit simplex of R^{α_0} and that K′ is isomorphic to K: Each r-simplex of K goes over into an r-simplex of K′, two simplexes σ^r and σ^s of K which are disjoint or have the common face σ^t go over, because of the independence of the unit points, into simplexes which are disjoint or have the image of σ^t as a common face.

In order to introduce the second realization, we first recall the following two theorems of elementary geometry of R^N. Any m points $\mathfrak{p}_j$ ($j = 1, \ldots, m$) of R^N are said to be in *general position* provided every subsystem of the $\mathfrak{p}_j$ of $N + 1$ or fewer points is independent. In particular, every independent point system is in general position. Then, as is well known, the following assertions hold:

A. If the points $\mathfrak{p}_j$ ($j = 1, \ldots, m$) of R^N are in general position, then there exist spherical neighborhoods $\mathfrak{U}_\varepsilon(\mathfrak{p}_j)$ of the $\mathfrak{p}_j$ such that every system of points $\mathfrak{q}_j$ with $\mathfrak{q}_j \in \mathfrak{U}_\varepsilon(\mathfrak{p}_j)$ is in general position.

B. If $\mathfrak{p}_j$ ($j = 1, \ldots, m$) are abritrary, but not necessarily distinct points of R^N, and if the $\mathfrak{U}_\varepsilon(\mathfrak{p}_j)$ are arbitrary spherical neighborhoods of the $\mathfrak{p}_j$, then there exist points $\mathfrak{q}_j \in \mathfrak{U}_\varepsilon(\mathfrak{p}_j)$ which taken together form a system in general position.

II. *Realization in* R^{2n+1}. Suppose the complex K of dimension n has the vertices $\mathfrak{p}_i$ ($i = 1, \ldots, \alpha_0$). In R^{2n+1} we choose α_0 points $\mathfrak{x}_i$ in general position and assign to each q-simplex σ^q of K, which is spanned by certain of the $\mathfrak{p}_i$, that simplex in R^{2n+1} which is spanned by the vertices $\mathfrak{x}_i$ with the same indices.

In this way, one obtains as the image K′ of K a simplicial complex which is really isomorphic to K: To each q-simplex of K and its $q + 1$ independent vertices there correspond $q + 1$ independent vertices in K′ and thus really a q-simplex. If σ^p and σ^q are disjoint simplexes of K, then their $(q + 1) + (p + 1)$ vertices correspond under this correspondence to certain vertices of K′ which because of their number $p + q + 2 \leqq 2n + 2$ are independent, and which therefore span disjoint image simplexes. If σ^p and σ^q have a σ^r as a common face, then for the same reason the same holds for the image simplexes in K′.

30.3 Definition: The field of a simplicial complex K of R^N, i.e. the set of points of all the simplexes of K equipped with the topology induced by R^N, is called a *rectilinear polyhedron* $R = |\,\mathsf{K}\,|$. K is called a *simplicial decomposition* or a *triangulation* of R. Every homeomorphic image of a rectilinear polyhedron $R = |\,\mathsf{K}\,|$ in an arbitrary Hausdorff space is called a (*curvilinear*) *polyhedron*; in this connection, the simplexes of K are called (*curvilinear*) *simplexes* and the image of K is called a (*curvilinear*) *triangulation* of the polyhedron.

By a polyhedron $R = |\,\mathsf{K}\,|$ without further requirements we therefore understand a curvilinear polyhedron. Curvilinear triangulations and simplexes for this reason will play a minor role for us inasmuch as we can study their properties just as well from their rectilinear preimages. A rectilinear polyhedron and thus also an arbitrary polyhedron is a compact space.

We note that by definition a polyhedron $R = |\,\mathsf{K}\,|$ is always given together with a triangulation K. If K and K′ are isomorphic simplicial complexes, then the corresponding polyhedra $|\,\mathsf{K}\,|$ and $|\,\mathsf{K}'\,|$ are obviously homeomorphic, since each pair of corresponding simplexes are, as simplexes of the same dimension, mapped on one another by an affine mapping and these affine mappings can obviously be combined into a homeomorphism of $|\,\mathsf{K}\,|$ and $|\,\mathsf{K}'\,|$. The converse of this theorem is not valid. Two distinct triangulations of the same polyhedron are not interrelated in a simple relation. Even two edges of a curvilinear polyhedron, for instance, can be situated with respect to one another as are the segment $-\pi \leqq x \leqq +\pi$ of the (x, y)-plane and the curve $y = x \sin \dfrac{1}{x}$ for $-\pi \leqq x \leqq +\pi$, augmented by $y = 0$ for $x = 0$, which have an infinite number of intersection points with one another. It is not immediately clear *a priori* whether a polyhedron can possess triangulations of different algebraic dimensions; in any case, we shall show in the last chapter that this is not the case. A polyhedron $R = |\mathsf{K}|$ carries a metric according to the embedding of K in the Euclidean space R^N, and therefore it is a metric space. The different metrics, which arise from the different realizations of K, are topologically equivalent (see Definition 2.3). The metric resulting from the unit representation of K is called the *unit metric* of $R = |\mathsf{K}|$.

Examples of polyhedra: (1) The points of an n-simplex $[\sigma] = [\sigma^n]$ form a polyhedron T^n with the triangulation T^n of example (1) associated with Definition 30.1. T^n is called an n-dimensional element; every homeomorphic image of T^n, for example, a closed n-dimensional sphere or a closed n-dimensional ellipsoid, is also called an n-dimensional element.

(2) The points on the proper (at most n-dimensional) faces of an $(n + 1)$-simplex σ^{n+1} form a polyhedron S^n with the triangulation $\sum^n$ of example (2) adjoined to Definition 30.1. S^n is called the n-dimensional sphere; also every homeomorphic image of S^n, for example, the boundary of an $(n + 1)$-dimensional ball is called an n-dimensional sphere.

The open simplexes of a triangulation K of the polyhedron $R = |\mathsf{K}|$ form, because of [S 2], a decomposition of R (cf. the Index). In regard to this, we make the following definition.

30.4 Definition: If $\mathfrak{x}$ is a point of the polyhedron $R = |\mathsf{K}|$ with the triangulation K, then the uniquely determined simplex of K which contains $\mathfrak{x}$ as an open simplex is called the *carrier simplex* or briefly the *carrier* of $\mathfrak{x}$.

30.5 Definition: Let $\mathfrak{p}$ be a vertex of the simplicial complex K. The set of all the points of the polyhedron $R = |\mathsf{K}|$, whose carrier simplex has $\mathfrak{p}$ as a vertex, is called the (*open*) *star*, *st* $\mathfrak{p}$, of $\mathfrak{p}$.

st $\mathfrak{p}$ is an open set in R. For, we have that *st* $\mathfrak{p} = R - |\mathsf{K}^*|$ where K^* is that simplicial complex which consists of all the simplexes of K which do not have $\mathfrak{p}$ as a vertex; $|\mathsf{K}^*|$ is closed and therefore *st* $\mathfrak{p}$ is open in R.

30.6 Theorem: *The vertices* $\mathfrak{p}_i$ $(i = 1, \ldots, m)$ *of a simplicial complex* K *are the vertices of the same simplexes of* K *if, and only if, the stars st* $\mathfrak{p}_i$ *have an intersection which is* $\neq \emptyset$.

Proof: If the vertices $\mathfrak{p}_i$ are situated on a simplex of K, then we obviously have that $\bigcap st\, \mathfrak{p}_i \neq \emptyset$. Conversely, if this inequality is satisfied and if $\mathfrak{x}$ is a point of this intersection, then all the $\mathfrak{p}_i$ lie on the carrier simplex of $\mathfrak{x}$.

§ 31. Subdivisions

By the *center of gravity* $\hat{\sigma} = \hat{\sigma}^n$ of a simplex $\sigma = \sigma^n = \mathfrak{p}_0 \ldots \mathfrak{p}_n$ we understand the point whose barycentric coordinates are all equal to $\dfrac{1}{n+1}$. The line connecting the centers of gravity of two opposite simplex faces of σ, say σ^r and σ^{n-r-1}, is called the *median* of σ. As a generalization of a well-known theorem about the medians of a triangle, we prove the following theorem.

31.1 Theorem: *The medians of a simplex* σ^n *pass through the center of gravity of* σ; *if a median joins the center of gravity of* σ^r *with the center of gravity of* σ^{n-r-1}, *then it is divided in the ratio* $(n - r) : (r + 1)$ *by* $\hat{\sigma}$.

Proof: The coordinates of the centers of gravity of σ^r and σ^{n-r-1} are, for a suitable numbering of the vertices of σ:

$$\hat{\sigma}^r: \left(\frac{1}{r+1}, \ldots, \frac{1}{r+1}, 0, \ldots, 0\right), \ (r + 1 \text{ zeros}),$$

$$\hat{\sigma}^{n-r-1}: \left(0, \ldots, 0, \frac{1}{n-r}, \ldots, \frac{1}{n-r}\right), \ (n - r \text{ zeros}).$$

Now one can form the vector $\hat{\sigma}$ which was just given as a linear combination of these two vectors and indeed with the factors $\dfrac{r+1}{n+1}$ and $\dfrac{n-r}{n+1}$, which make evident the asserted division ratio.

31.2 Definition: Let K be a rectilinear simplicial complex. The simplicial complex K′ is called a *subdivision* of K if the following two conditions are satisfied:

[*T* 1] | K′ | = | K |, *i.e. the corresponding polyhedra are identical;*

[*T* 2] *Each open simplex* (σ') *of* K′ *is contained in an open simplex* (σ) *of* K.

The concept of a subdivision carries over, meaningfully, to curvilinear simplicial complexes.

31.3 Theorem: *For every rectilinear simplicial complex* K *there exists a subdivision* K′, *the so-called normal subdivision of* K, *with the following properties:*

(a) *The vertices of* K′ *are the centers of gravity* $\hat{\sigma}$ *of the simplexes* σ *of* K.

(b) *The vertices* $\hat{\sigma}_0, \ldots, \hat{\sigma}_m$ *are the vertices of a simplex* $\sigma' = \sigma'^m$ *of* K′ *if, and only if, the corresponding simplexes* $\sigma_0, \ldots, \sigma_m$ *of* K *form, with a suitable numbering, an incidence sequence* $\sigma_0 \prec \sigma_1 \prec \ldots \prec \sigma_m$.

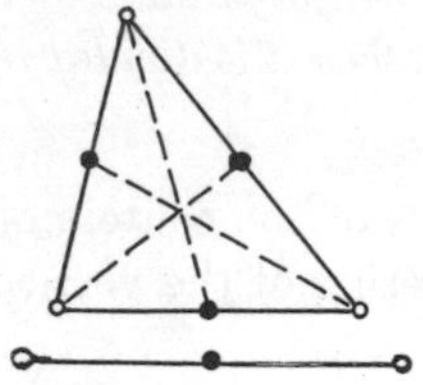

Fig. 7

In Figure 7, T^1 and T^2 are pointed out as examples of normal subdivisions of complexes, which correspond to the segment σ^1 and the triangle σ^2 (in the sense of the example associated with Definition 30.1).

We preface the proof with several observations. If $\sigma_0 \prec \sigma_1 \prec \ldots \prec \sigma_m$, then all the vertices $\sigma_0, \ldots, \sigma_m$ lie in $[\sigma_m]$; all the $\sigma_0, \ldots, \sigma_m$ are simplex faces of σ_m. If we write down the barycentric coordinates of $\hat{\sigma}_0, \ldots, \hat{\sigma}_m$ (with the vertices of σ^m as reference points), we recognize the independence of the coordinate vectors and thus (§ 29, 5.) the independence of the points $\hat{\sigma}_0, \ldots, \hat{\sigma}_m$; thus, (b) really determines the simplexes $\sigma' = \hat{\sigma}_0 \ldots \hat{\sigma}_m$. More specifically, we recognize thereby that $(\sigma') \subset (\sigma_m)$. To this end, we must identify the points $\mathfrak{x}_k$ ($k = 1, \ldots, m$) with the $\hat{\sigma}_k$. If the point $\mathfrak{z}$ lies in (σ'), i.e. all the μ_k are > 0, then all the $\bar{\lambda}_i$ are also > 0, i.e. $\mathfrak{z}$ lies in (σ_m).

The vertices $\hat{\sigma}_i$ of a simplex σ' of K' allow, according to (b), a natural correspondence, namely, according to the dimension ν_i of the corresponding simplexes $\sigma_i = \sigma_i^{\nu_i}$. $\hat{\sigma}_0$ is called the "first" vertex of σ', $\hat{\sigma}_m$ is called the "last" vertex of σ'. We can make this explicitly clear for all the simplexes σ' of the above figure.

We must prove that the simplexes σ' form a simplicial complex K', i.e. that [S 1] and [S 2] hold and further that K' is a subdivision of K, i.e. that [T 1] and [T 2] hold. [S 1] is evident according to the construction of K', namely, according to (b). We have just proved [T 2] by means of the relation $(\sigma') \subset (\sigma_m)$. Both remaining assertions [S 2] and [T 1] are indeed intuitively evident, but for a rigorous proof they require the following theorem which is not so evident.

31.4 Theorem: *Let $\mathfrak{s}$ be a point of the simplex (σ). The following assertions are valid: (a) If $\mathfrak{x}$, $\mathfrak{y}$, $\mathfrak{x} \neq \mathfrak{y}$, are two points of $\dot{\sigma}$, then the open intervals $(\mathfrak{s}\mathfrak{x})$ and $(\mathfrak{s}\mathfrak{y})$ have no points in common. (b) Every point $\mathfrak{z}$ distinct from $\mathfrak{s}$ of the open simplex (σ) lies in an open interval $(\mathfrak{s}\mathfrak{z})$ with suitable $\mathfrak{x} \in \dot{\sigma}$.* [$\dot{\sigma}$ is defined in Definition 29.1.]

In toto, the theorem asserts that the projection rays completely fill the simplex without intersections from $\mathfrak{s}$ to the boundary $\dot{\sigma}$ of the simplex.

Proof: (a) Let $\mathfrak{s} = \sum \lambda_i \mathfrak{p}_i$, $\sum \lambda_i = 1$, where we always sum over $i = 0, \ldots, n$, $\lambda_i > 0$. Let $\mathfrak{x} = \sum \xi_i \mathfrak{p}_i$, $\sum \xi_i = 1$, $\xi_i \geqq 0$, lie on $\dot{\sigma}$ so that $\xi_j = 0$ for at least one index. Likewise, let $\mathfrak{y} = \sum \eta_i \mathfrak{p}_i$, $\sum \eta_i = 1$, $\eta_i \geqq 0$, η_k, $= 0$ lie on $\dot{\sigma}$. Let $\mathfrak{z}$ be a point common to $(\mathfrak{s}\mathfrak{x})$ and $(\mathfrak{s}\mathfrak{y})$; then

$$\mathfrak{z} = \alpha\mathfrak{x} + (1 - \alpha)\mathfrak{s} = \beta\mathfrak{y} + (1 - \beta)\mathfrak{s} \text{ with } 0 < \alpha < 1,\ 0 < \beta < 1.$$

For the two distinguished indexes j and k, this signifies in barycentric coordinates that

$$(1 - \alpha)\lambda_j = \beta\eta_j + (1 - \beta)\lambda_j, \text{ and hence that } (\beta - \alpha)\lambda_j = \beta\eta_j,$$

$$\alpha\xi_k + (1 - \alpha)\lambda_k = (1 - \beta)\lambda_k, \text{ and hence that } (\alpha - \beta)\lambda_k = \alpha\xi_k.$$

Since λ_j, λ_k, α, $\beta > 0$ and η_j, $\xi_k \geqq 0$, it follows that $\beta \geqq \alpha$, $\alpha \geqq \beta$, $\alpha = \beta$. It follows from the representation of $\mathfrak{z}$ that $\alpha\mathfrak{x} = \alpha\mathfrak{y}$ and that $\mathfrak{x} = \mathfrak{y}$, contrary to our assumption; therefore, there does not exist a $\mathfrak{z}$ of the assumed sort.

(b) Let $\mathfrak{z} = \sum\zeta_i\mathfrak{p}_i$, $\sum\zeta_i = 1$, $\zeta_i > 0$. We must find a point $\mathfrak{x}$ with

$$\mathfrak{x} = \alpha\mathfrak{z} + (1 - \alpha)\mathfrak{s} \text{ and } \mathfrak{x} \in \dot{\sigma}.$$

In barycentric coordinates, this signifies that α is to be determined so that

$$\xi_i = \alpha\zeta_i + (1 - \alpha)\lambda_i = \alpha(\zeta_i - \lambda_i) + \lambda_i \begin{cases} = 0 \text{ for at least one } i, \\ \geqq 0 \text{ for all } i. \end{cases}$$

Since not all $\zeta_i = \lambda_i$, there exist indices i with solutions α for the equation; since $\sum\zeta_i = \sum\lambda_i = 1$, there even exist indices with $\zeta_i - \lambda_i < 0$ and therefore positive solutions α. We now fix α as the smallest positive solution; suppose it occurs for the index j so that

$$\xi_j = \alpha(\zeta_j - \lambda_j) + \lambda_j = 0.$$

Let $\mathfrak{x}$ be fixed in a corresponding manner. If $\zeta_i - \lambda_i \geqq 0$, then $\xi_i = \alpha(\zeta_i - \lambda_i) + \lambda_i \geqq 0$. For the indices i with $\zeta_i - \lambda_i < 0$. there exists an $\bar{\alpha}$ with $\bar{\alpha}(\zeta_i - \lambda_i) + \lambda_i = 0$ and, because of the choice of α as minimal, surely $\bar{\alpha} \geqq \alpha > 0$. From this it follows that $\xi_i = \alpha(\zeta_i - \lambda_i) + \lambda_i \geqq 0$. Thus, in reality $\mathfrak{x} \in \dot{\sigma}$. Moreover,

$$\mathfrak{z} = \frac{1}{\alpha}\mathfrak{x} + \left(1 - \frac{1}{\alpha}\right)\mathfrak{s}$$

with $1 - \dfrac{1}{\alpha} = \dfrac{\zeta_j}{\lambda_j} > 0$. This completes the proof of the theorem.

We now conclude the proof of Theorem 31.3 by proving the remaining assertions [S 2] and [T 1] by induction on the dimension q of the q-dimensional skeleton K_q of $\mathsf{K} = \mathsf{K}_n$. For $q = 0$, $\mathsf{K}_0 = (\mathsf{K}_0)'$; hence, $|\mathsf{K}_0| = |(\mathsf{K}_0)'|$ and there is nothing to prove. Suppose [S 2] and [T 1] have already been proved for $(\mathsf{K}_q)'$. K_{q+1} arises from K_q by the adjunction of the $(q + 1)$-dimensional simplexes σ^{q+1} of K. $(\mathsf{K}_{q+1})'$ arises from $(\mathsf{K}_q)'$ by the adjunction of the vertices σ^{q+1} and all the simplexes σ' of K' which have a σ^{q+1} as last vertex. For these σ', $(\sigma') \subset (\sigma^{q+1})$; therefore, these (σ') have no point in common with any open simplex of $(\mathsf{K}_q)'$. They also have no points in common among themselves, inasmuch as they consist, since their dimension is > 0

(cf. Theorem 29.3), of the points of the open intervals $(\mathfrak{x}\sigma^{q+1})$ with an $\mathfrak{x}$ from a (σ_q') in $(\mathsf{K}_q)'$; these (σ') are by our induction assumption disjoint so that the (σ') are disjoint by part (a) of the last theorem. Thus $[S\,2]$ is proved for $(\mathsf{K}_{q+1})'$.

In order to prove $[T\,1]$ for $(\mathsf{K}_{q+1})'$, it suffices, since $[T\,2]$ is already proved, to show that $|\,(\mathsf{K}_{q+1})'\,| \supset |\,\mathsf{K}_{q+1}\,|$. Therefore, on the basis of our induction assumption, we have still to show that every point of a (σ^{q+1}) occurs in $|\,(\mathsf{K}_{q+1})'\,|$. But part (b) of the last theorem shows this. This completes the proof of Theorem 31.3.

31.5 Theorem: *If the simplex σ^n has the diameter d, then every simplex σ' of the normal subdivision $\mathsf{T}^{n\prime}$ of the simplicial complex T^n of all faces of σ^n has diameter $\leqq \dfrac{n}{n+1}\,d$.*

The *proof* is by induction. For $n = 0$, the theorem is trivial. Suppose it has already been proved for dimensions $0, 1, \ldots, n - 1$. According to Theorem 29.2, we have to show that the length of the longest edge of the normal subdivision of T^n satisfies the inequality of the theorem. The edges which lie on a boundary face of σ^n are, according to the induction assumption, at most of length equal to $\dfrac{n-1}{n}d$. This number is in fact $\leqq \dfrac{n}{n+1}\,d$. Edges of the normal subdivision of T^n which lie in the interior of the open simplex (σ^n) arise from the medians of σ^n by division in the center of gravity $\hat{\sigma}^n$. The entire medians have a length $\leqq d$; each of their parts has, according to Theorem 31.1, at most the length

$$\frac{n-r}{n+1}d \leqq \frac{n}{n+1}d \text{ or } \frac{r+1}{n+1}d \leqq \frac{n}{n+1}d$$

for $r = 0, \ldots, n - 1$. This completes the proof of the theorem.

One can iterate further the process of the normal subdivision of a simplicial complex K and thus obtain the second normal subdivision K'' and the further ν-th normal subdivisions $\mathsf{K}^{(\nu)}$ of K ($\nu = 1, 2, \ldots$). If K is n-dimensional and the diameter any simplex of K is at most equal to d, then the diameter of all simplexes of K' is at most equal to $\dfrac{n}{n+1}d$ and the diameter of all the simplexes of the ν-th normal subdivision $\mathsf{K}^{(\nu)}$ of K is at most $\left(\dfrac{n}{n+1}\right)^{\nu} d$. Since this expression tends to zero as ν increases, we can state the following theorem.

31.6 Theorem: *The diameters of the simplexes of the ν-th normal subdivision $\mathsf{K}^{(\nu)}$ of a complex K tend to zero uniformly as ν increases to ∞.*

Chapter 10

DIMENSION OF COMPACTA

§ 32. Paving Dimension

In this chapter, we pose the problem of how to assign to a topological space $\mathfrak{X}$ an integer n as "dimension," $\dim \mathfrak{X} = n$. Naturally, the definition should depend only on the space $\mathfrak{X}$ and its topology $\mathfrak{T}$ but not, for example, on a metric on $\mathfrak{X}$ based on the topology $\mathfrak{T}$. By the definition, homeomorphic spaces should be assigned the same dimension, i.e. dimension should be a topological invariant. It turns out that this problem contains many more difficult problems than may appear at first glance. For example, if we require—as is natural—that the dimension of a simplex σ^n of the algebraic dimension n be precisely $\dim \sigma^n = n$, then the problem arises—according to our previous deliberations—whether two simplexes σ^m and σ^n with $m \neq n$ can be homeomorphic. If this were the case, then there would be no dimension concept of the type outlined.

However improbable it now appears that, say, $[\sigma^m]$ and $[\sigma^n]$ could be homeomorphic for $m \neq n$—that there could exist a one-to-one continuous mapping f of $[\sigma^m]$ onto $[\sigma^n]$ such that f^{-1} is also continuous—the following two possibilities are still, however, conceivable:

(I) There exists a one-to-one mapping f of $[\sigma^m]$ onto $[\sigma^n]$, at least one which may not be continuous. Such mappings are considered in set theory (see, for instance, E. Kamke [1], §§ 11, 12, in particular, p. 43), where the example $f\colon \sigma^1 \to \sigma^2$ is discussed in detail.

(II) For arbitrary m and n, there exists an epimorphic continuous mapping f of $[\sigma^m]$ onto $[\sigma^n]$, at least one which may not be one to one.

In the case $m = 1, n = 2$, such mappings are given by the so-called Peano curves (for example, see F. HAUSDORFF [2], § 36). We shall later prove that one can even represent every non-empty compactum as a continuous image of the zero-dimensional Cantor discontinuum (cf. Theorem 32.2).

It was not excluded *a priori* that one could construct a one-to-one and continuous mapping of $[\sigma^m]$ onto $[\sigma^n]$ by combining the characteristic features of both examples. That this is in reality impossible was first shown in 1911 by L. E. J. Brouwer (cf. *Beweis der Invarianz der Dimensionszahl*, Math. Ann. 70, 161–165). Brouwer proved the following theorem.

32.1 Theorem: *Two simplexes* $[\sigma^m]$ *and* $[\sigma^n]$ *of different (algebraic) dimensions* m *and* n *are not homeomorphic.*

With the proof of this theorem, dimension theory began as an independent discipline of topology. We shall prove this theorem within the framework of a more comprehensive theory, by introducing a dimension concept, on the basis of a topologically invariant property which is defined for arbitrary compacta, which assigns, in particular, to a simplex $[\sigma^n]$ the dimension n. One knows today very many such properties which characterize dimension; we stop on the first one, historically speaking, discovered by H. Lebesgue in 1913, i.e. the "paving property" which distinguishes itself by its simplicity and elementary geometrical intuitiveness. It is based on the following concept.

32.2 Definition: The natural number $o \geqq 1$ is called the *order* of the covering $\mathfrak{D} = \{D_\lambda \mid \lambda \text{ from an arbitrary index set } \Lambda\}$ of the space $\mathfrak{X} \neq \varnothing$ if there exists at least one point $p \in \mathfrak{X}$ which belongs to o distinct sets D_λ but no point of $\mathfrak{X}$ belongs to more than o sets D_λ. If there does not exist a natural number o of this sort, then $\mathfrak{D}$ is said to be of *infinite* order.

We now recall how one paves a street with square paving stones—not so that a quadratic lattice is formed, but rather displaced one with respect to another, row by row, as is apparent from Fig. 8. If

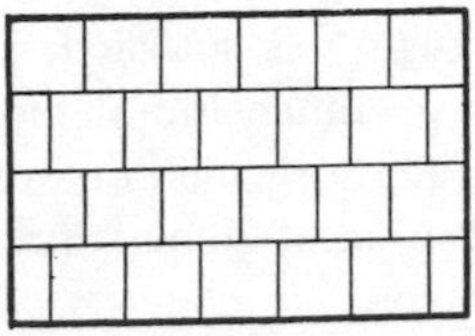

Fig. 8

one thinks of the figure as a covering of a rectangle by small closed squares, then one sees that the order of the covering is 3. It is accordingly plausible that a plane rectangle admits an ε-covering of order 3 for every $\varepsilon > 0$. It likewise naturally admits coverings of order 4, 5, and so on; but one would exert himself in vain if one tried to form ε-coverings of order 2 with small ε. One can picture analogous considerations in the space R^3; here, one would find ε-coverings of a 3-dimensional square of order 4, 5, and so on, but none of order 2 or even 3. These considerations motivate the following definition of the paving dimension of a space $\mathfrak{X}$. We must limit ourselves within the framework of this little volume to compacta $\mathfrak{X}$.

32.3 Definition: The integer n is called the *dimension* of the compactum $\mathfrak{X}$, $\dim \mathfrak{X} = n$, if $\mathfrak{X}$ possesses the following two properties:

(a_n) For every $\varepsilon > 0$ there exists a finite closed ε-covering of $\mathfrak{X}$ with order $\leqq n + 1$.

(b_n) There exists an $\varepsilon > 0$ such that every finite closed ε-covering of $\mathfrak{X}$ has an order $\geqq n + 1$.

A compactum $\mathfrak{X}$ which does not possess the property (a_n) for any n is called *infinite dimensional.*

For the understanding of this definition, let the following be noted. It is clear that by this definition, every non-empty compactum $\mathfrak{X}$ is assigned a well-defined dimension, namely, infinite dimension or an integer $n = 0, 1, 2, \ldots$ as dimension. (The empty set $\varnothing$ is usually assigned the dimension -1.) The property (a_n) asserts that $\mathfrak{X}$ has dimension at most n, i.e. that $\dim \mathfrak{X} \leqq n$; the property ($b_n$) asserts that $\mathfrak{X}$ has dimension at least n, i.e. that $\dim \mathfrak{X} \geqq n$.

One could also make the following definition: dim $\mathfrak{X} = n$ if the property (a_n), but not (a_{n-1}), is satisfied, i.e. if $\mathfrak{X}$ has dimension at most n but does not have dimension at most $n - 1$. In fact, (b_n) is exactly the negation of (a_{n-1}), which one can make explicitly clear. The shortest formal definition would be: dim $\mathfrak{X} = n$ if n is the smallest integer for which (a_n) holds.

We shall first show that dimension so defined is a topological invariant. To this end, we must show that: If $\mathfrak{X}$ and $\mathfrak{X}'$ are compacta with dim $\mathfrak{X} = n$ and if $f\colon \mathfrak{X} \to \mathfrak{X}'$ is a one-to-one continuous mapping of $\mathfrak{X}$ onto $\mathfrak{X}'$, then dim $\mathfrak{X}' = n$. Because of the uniform continuity of f (cf. Theorem 25.1) one can determine, for given $\varepsilon > 0$, a $\delta = \delta(\varepsilon)$ so that $d(f(x), f(y)) < \frac{\varepsilon}{2}$ holds for $d(x, y) < \delta$, and $x, y \in \mathfrak{X}$. If $\mathfrak{D} = \{D_i \mid i = 1, \ldots, m\}$ is a finite closed δ-covering of $\mathfrak{X}$ of order $n + 1$, then $\{f(D_i) \mid i = 1, \ldots, m\}$ is likewise a finite closed covering of $\mathfrak{X}'$ of order $n + 1$. $d(D_i) < \delta$ implies that $d(f(D_i)) \leqq \frac{\varepsilon}{2} < \varepsilon$. (a_n) is thus proved for $\mathfrak{X}'$, from which it follows that dim $\mathfrak{X}' \leqq n =$ dim $\mathfrak{X}$. In exactly the same way, it follows that dim $\mathfrak{X} \leqq$ dim $\mathfrak{X}'$ so that dim $\mathfrak{X}' =$ dim $\mathfrak{X}$.

If $\mathfrak{X}$ has infinite dimension, then by this $\mathfrak{X}'$ also has infinite dimension. This completes the proof of our assertion.

32.4 Thereom: *If $\mathfrak{X}$ and $\mathfrak{X}'$ are compacta, $\mathfrak{X} \subset \mathfrak{X}'$, then dim $\mathfrak{X} \leqq$ dim $\mathfrak{X}'$.*

Proof: Suppose dim $\mathfrak{X}' = n$. For each $\varepsilon > 0$ there exists a finite closed ε-covering of $\mathfrak{X}'$ of order $n + 1$. This induces in $\mathfrak{X}$ a finite closed ε-covering of at most the same order, from which it follows that dim $\mathfrak{X} \leqq$ dim $\mathfrak{X}'$.

We will further prove that in Definition 32.3 one can also use open coverings in place of closed coverings. To this end, we need two theorems which compare open and closed coverings of a compactum. Both depend on Theorem 24.3.

32.5 Theorem: (Refinement of Open Coverings): *If $\mathfrak{D} = \{D_i \mid i = 1,$*

. . . , m\} is a finite open covering of the compactum $\mathfrak{X}$, *then there exists a closed covering* $\mathfrak{F} = \{F_i \mid i = 1, \ldots, m\}$ *with* $F_i \subset D_i$ *for* $i = 1, \ldots, m$.

Proof: The system of closed sets $\complement D_i$ has intersection $\emptyset$ so that one can apply Theorem 24.3 to it. According to Theorem 24.3, there exist open sets $F'_i \supset \complement D_i$ which also have intersection $\emptyset$. The sets $\complement F'_i \subset F_i$ are therefore closed, they cover $\mathfrak{X}$, and we have that $F_i \subset D_i$; this completes the proof of the theorem.

32.6 Theorem: (Enlargement of Closed Coverings): *If* $\mathfrak{D} = \{D_i \mid i = 1, \ldots, m\}$ *is a finite closed covering of the compactum* $\mathfrak{X}$, *then there exists a* $\delta > 0$ *such that the open covering* $\mathfrak{D}_\delta$ *and the closed covering* $\overline{\mathfrak{D}}_\delta$,

$$\mathfrak{D}_\delta = \{\mathfrak{U}_\delta(D_i) \mid i = 1, \ldots, m\}, \overline{\mathfrak{D}}_\delta = \{\overline{\mathfrak{U}_\delta(D_i)} \mid i = 1, \ldots, m\},$$

have the same order as $\mathfrak{D}$.

Proof: Let $\mathfrak{D}$ have the order o. Since the order can at most increase for an enlargement of the sets D_i, it suffices to show that, for suitable δ, $\overline{\mathfrak{D}}_\delta$ also has an order $\leqq o$.

Every subsystem of $\mathfrak{D}$ consisting of $o + 1$ of the sets D_i has intersection $\emptyset$. By Theorem 24.3, there exists an $\varepsilon > 0$ such that the corresponding sets $\overline{\mathfrak{U}_\varepsilon(D_i)}$ have intersection $\emptyset$. If one finds for each subsystem of $\mathfrak{D}$ of the indicated sort an associated real number ε and chooses δ as the smallest of these ε, then each collection of $o + 1$ sets of the form $\overline{\mathfrak{U}_\delta(D_i)}$ has intersection $\emptyset$. This means that the order of $\overline{\mathfrak{D}}_\delta$ is at most o, which is what we were required to prove.

32.7 Theorem: *In Definition* 32.3 *of the dimension of a compactum* $\mathfrak{X}$, *the word "closed" can be replaced by the word "open."*

Proof: We denote the conditions (a_n) and (b_n) of Definition 32.3 by (a'_n) and (b'_n) respectively if in them "closed" is replaced by "open." We first prove that under the assumption that $\dim \mathfrak{X} = n$, (b'_n) as well as (a'_n) holds.

(a'_n) Let $\varepsilon > 0$ be given. According to (a_n), there exists a finite closed $\frac{\varepsilon}{2}$-covering $\mathfrak{D}$ of $\mathfrak{X}$ of order $\leqq n + 1$. According to Theorem 32.6, for suitable $\delta > 0$, $\mathfrak{D}_\delta$ also has order $\leqq n + 1$. If one chooses δ furthermore so that $\delta < \frac{\varepsilon}{4}$, then the sets from $\mathfrak{D}_\delta$ surely have diameter $< \varepsilon$, and hence represent an ε-covering of the sort required in (a'_n).

(b'_n) Let ε be chosen in accordance with (b_n). If $\mathfrak{D}$ is a finite open ε-covering of $\mathfrak{X}$, then by Theorem 32.5 there exists a closed ε-covering $\mathfrak{F}$

whose sets are eventually contained in those of $\mathfrak{D}$ and which thus have diameter $< \varepsilon$. According to (b_n), $\mathfrak{F}$ has order $\geqq n + 1$ and this holds *a fortiori* for $\mathfrak{D}$.

If $\mathfrak{X}$ is infinite dimensional, one shows in an exactly analogous fashion that $\mathfrak{X}$ does not satisfy (a_n') for any integer n.

Conversely, we now assume that the conditions (a_n') and (b_n') are satisfied. Then if $\dim \mathfrak{X} = m$, (a_m) and $b_m)$ hold and so, according to the first part of the proof, (a_m') and (b_m') follow. Since, however, the number n is uniquely determined by (a_n') and (b_n'), it follows that $m = n$. This completes the proof of the theorem.

§ 33. Zero-Dimensional Compacta

Compacta of dimension 0 can be described relatively easily, as we shall see in this section. For a non-empty compactum $\mathfrak{X}$ to have dimension 0, condition (a_0) in the definition of dimension in the preceding section is obviously sufficient. It asserts that for each $\varepsilon > 0$, there exists a finite closed ε-covering of $\mathfrak{X}$ of order 1, i.e. a covering by disjoint sets.

The following are examples of zero-dimensional compacta:

(a) a finite number of points with the discrete topology;

(b) the set of numbers $0, \frac{1}{n}$ $(n = 1, 2, \ldots)$ on the real line;

(c) the Cantor discontinuum $\mathscr{C}$; we have already established the zero-dimensionality of $\mathscr{C}$ in § 9 as property (6).

33.1 Theorem: *A non-empty compactum $\mathfrak{X}$ is zero-dimensional if, and only if, any one of the following three equivalent conditions is satisfied:*

(1) *For each $\varepsilon > 0$, there exists a finite closed ε-covering of $\mathfrak{X}$ consisting of disjoint sets.*

(2) *For each pair of points $x, y, x \neq y$, from $\mathfrak{X}$, there exist open-closed subsets A, B of $\mathfrak{X}$ with $x \in A, y \in B$.*

(3) *$\mathfrak{X}$ is totally disconnected.*

In condition (1), *the word "closed" can also be replaced by "open" and also by "open-closed."*

Proof: (1) is the condition (a_0) in the definition of dimension. A covering set D from the covering (1) is open, since it is the complement of the union of the remaining finitely many closed covering sets; every D is therefore open-closed, as is asserted at the end of the theorem.

(1) $\Rightarrow$ (2) Let $d(x, y) = \varepsilon > 0$. Every ε-covering yields according to (1) a covering set A with $x \in A$, but, because $d(A) < \varepsilon, y \notin A$ and

analogously a covering set B with $y \in B$, $x \notin B$. A and B are of the required sort.

(2) $\Rightarrow$ (3) Let $x \in \mathfrak{X}$ and $C(x)$ be the connectivity components of x. For every $y \in \mathfrak{X}$, $y \neq x$, there exists according to (2) an open-closed set A with $x \in A$, $y \notin A$. $C(x) \subset A$ (compare the remark before Theorem 7.9); therefore, $y \notin C(x)$. $C(x)$ therefore contains no point y different from x, which is what we were required to prove.

(3) $\Rightarrow$(1) Let $x \in \mathfrak{X}$ and let U be an open neighborhood of x. For every real number $\eta > 0$ we consider the η-components $C_\eta(x)$ whose union is an open-closed set (see the proof of Theorem 24.4). If η ranges over a monotonically decreasing null sequence, then the $C_\eta(x)$ form a decreasing sequence of closed sets in the interior of the compactum $\mathfrak{X}$, and the same holds for the closed sets $C_\eta(x) - U$. If all the $C_\eta(x) - U$ were non-empty, then they would have a common point; however, the intersection $\bigcap C_\eta(x)$ of all the $C_\eta(x)$ equals the connectivity component $C(x)$ (cf. Theorem 24.6), which, according to (3), consists of x only, so that certainly $C(x) - U = \emptyset$ holds. Therefore $C_\eta(x) - U$ is empty for sufficiently small η, i.e., $C_\eta(x) = U$ for these η. We thus have the present result: The η-component $C_\eta(x)$ of a point $x \in \mathfrak{X}$ has an arbitrarily small diameter for sufficiently small η.

Now let ε be the real number indicated in the assertion (1). To each $x \in \mathfrak{X}$ we assign an η-component $C_\eta(x)$ with $d(C_\eta(x)) < \varepsilon$ which is possible, according to what we have already proved, by means of a suitable choice of η. These $C_\eta(x)$ form an open covering of $\mathfrak{X}$, from which one can select a finite covering

$$\mathfrak{D} = \{D_i \mid i = 1, \ldots, m\}$$

which consequently consists of open-closed sets D_i with $d(D_i) < \varepsilon$. We then have that

$$\mathfrak{D}' = \{D_1, D_2 - D_1, D_3 - (D_1 \cup D_2), \ldots, D_m - (D_1 \cup \ldots \cup D_{m-1})\}$$

is likewise a closed ε-covering and indeed one which consists of disjoint sets having a diameter $< \varepsilon$, as was required in (1).

In the preceding section, we have, by mentioning the Peano curves, pointed out that for continuous mappings the dimension can increase. We shall show that one can even map the zero-dimensional Cantor discontinuum $\mathscr{C}$ continuously onto a cube of arbitrarily high dimension, onto the ∞-dimensional Hilbert parallelepiped, and onto an arbitrary compactum.

33.2 Theorem: *Every non-empty compactum $\mathfrak{X}$ is a continuous image of the Cantor discontinuum.*

Proof: Being a totally bounded space, $\mathfrak{X}$ admits for every real $\varepsilon > 0$ finite ε-coverings $\mathfrak{D} = \{D_i \mid i = 1, \ldots, n\}$. In this connection, one can consider the D_i as closed since otherwise one can replace the D_i by $\overline{D}_i$ and then $d(D_i) = d(\overline{D}_i)$.

We first consider a covering $\mathfrak{D}_1 = \{D_{i_1} \mid i_1 = 1, \ldots, n_1 = 2^{m_1}\}$ of $\mathfrak{X}$ by non-empty closed D_{i_1} having diameters $< \frac{1}{2}$. We note here that $\mathfrak{X}$ is non-empty and that we can extend the number n of the covering sets to an arbitrary power of 2, say 2^{m_1}, if one agrees to admit equal sets D_i in $\mathfrak{D}$ and in the enumeration certain sets D_{i_1} are repeated. Every D_{i_1} is itself a non-empty compactum. We cover it by 2^{m_2} non-empty closed sets $D_{i_1 i_2}$ $(i_2 = 1, \ldots, 2^{m_2})$ with $d(D_{i_1 i_2}) < \frac{1}{2^2}$. Also the number of these covering sets can be increased to the same power of 2, say 2^{m_2}, for all D_{i_1}. There results a covering $\mathfrak{D}_2 = \{D_{i_1 i_2} \mid i_1 = 1, \ldots, 2^{m_1}; i_2 = 1, \ldots, 2^{m_2}\}$ of $\mathfrak{X}$ by $n_2 = 2^{m_1+m_2}$ sets. Continuing in this way, we obtain, for each $r = 1, 2, \ldots,$ a covering

$$\mathfrak{D}_r = \{D_{i_1 \cdots i_r} \mid i_\nu = 1, \ldots, 2^{m_\nu} \text{ with } \nu = 1, \ldots, r\}$$

of $\mathfrak{X}$ by $n_r = 2^{m_1 + \cdots + m_r}$ non-empty compacta having a diameter $< \frac{1}{2^r}$.

We now introduce a modification in the definition of the Cantor discontinuum $\mathscr{C}$ (see § 9) in order to be able to compare it easily with our compactum $\mathfrak{X}$. In the definition of $\mathscr{C}$, we consider the C-intervals of rank m_1 and denote them in a way which is changed with respect to § 9 by C^{i_1} $(i_1 = 1, \ldots, 2^{m_1})$ in their natural ordering on the interval $[0, 1]$. Further, we consider the $n_2 = 2^{m_1+m_2}$ C-intervals of rank $(m_1 + m_2)$. In each C^{i_1}, there are contained 2^{m_2} of them which are now denoted correspondingly by $C^{i_1 i_2}$ $(i_2 = 1, \ldots, 2^{m_2})$. In an analogous manner, the $n_r = 2^{m_1 + \cdots + m_r}$ C-intervals of rank $(m_1 + \ldots + m_r)$ are denoted by $C^{i_1 \cdots i_r}$. Let $C^{(m_1 + \cdots + m_r)}$ be as before the union of all C-intervals of rank $(m_1 + \ldots + m_r)$. Then

$$\mathscr{C} = \bigcap_{r=1}^{\infty} C^{(m_1 + \cdots + m_r)}.$$

We have that $d(C^{i_1 \cdots i_r}) = \frac{1}{3^{m_1 + \cdots + m_r}}$. The points $x \in \mathscr{C}$ are determined in one-to-one fashion by sequences $C^{i_1} \supset C^{i_1 i_2} \supset \ldots$ and by sequences $(i_1 i_2 \ldots)$ respectively where $x \in C^{i_1 \cdots i_r}$ and now i_ν ranges over the values $1, \ldots, 2^{m_\nu}$.

Now let x be an arbitrary point of $\mathscr{C}$ with the corresponding sequence $(i_1 i_2 \ldots)$. The sequence of decreasing compacta

$$D_{i_1} \supset D_{i_1 i_2} \supset \ldots$$

in $\mathfrak{X}$ then determines uniquely a point $p \in \mathfrak{X}$ which is contained in all these sets, which we denote as the image $p = f(x)$ of x. We assert that f is an epimorphic mapping onto $\mathfrak{X}$ which furthermore is continuous. With the proof of this assertion, the theorem is then proved.

If $p_0 \in \mathfrak{X}$ is arbitrarily prescribed, then one determines a D_{i_1} with $p_0 \in D_{i_1}$, next a $D_{i_1 i_2}$ (with the same i_1) with $p_0 \in D_{i_1 i_2}$, and continuing in this manner a sequence $D_{i_1} \supset D_{i_1 i_2} \supset \ldots$ which contains the single common point x_0. Then we seek out in $\mathscr{C}$ the uniquely determined point x_0 which is common to the sequence $C^{i_1} \supset C^{i_1 i_2} \supset \ldots$. We obviously have that $p_0 = f(x_0)$, which completes the proof that f is epimorphic.

Further, let $\varepsilon > 0$ be given and let r be so large that $\frac{1}{2^r} < \varepsilon$. As above, let $p_0 = f(x_0)$. Every x with $d(x, x_0) < \frac{1}{3^{m_1 + \cdots + m_r}}$ lies together with x_0 in the same set $C^{i_1 \cdots i_r}$. Therefore $p = f(x)$ and p_0 both lie in $D_{i_1 \ldots i_r}$, and hence we have that $d(p, p_0) \leqq d(D_{i_1 \ldots i_r}) < \frac{1}{2^r} < \varepsilon$. This also proves the continuity of f and thus the theorem is completely proved.

An infinite number of isolated points cannot form a compactum; but a compactum can very well contain an infinite number of isolated points, as the example (b) at the beginning of this section shows. Among all compacta, those without isolated points are of special interest. In this spirit, we give the following definition.

33.3 Definition: A zero-dimensional (non-empty) compactum $\mathfrak{X}$ without isolated points is called a *discontinuum*.

The Cantor discontinuum $\mathscr{C}$ whose nomenclature "discontinuum" is consequently in agreement with Definition 33.3 forms an example. Now the theorem asserting that from the topological standpoint all discontinua are already exhausted by $\mathscr{C}$ holds.

33.4 Theorem: *Every discontinuum $\mathfrak{X}$ is homeomorphic to the Cantor discontinuum.*

The proof consists in a sharpening of the considerations of the preceding proof. We first assert that: For every $\varepsilon > 0$, $\mathfrak{X}$ admits ε-coverings $\mathfrak{D} = \{D_i \mid i = 1, \ldots, r\}$ by (non-empty) disjoint open-closed discontinua D_i, the number of which equals a sufficiently high power of 2, say 2^m. One first recognizes that because of its zero dimensionality, $\mathfrak{X}$ allows finite closed ε-coverings by non-empty disjoint sets D_i. Each D_i is zero-dimensional and, being the complement of the union of the remaining finitely many covering sets, it is also open, and therefore open-closed.

No D_i, regarded as a subspace equipped with the topology induced by $\mathfrak{X}$ in D_i, has isolated points. Namely, if we suppose that p were such a point, then there would exist a D_i-neighborhood U of p containing no points of D_i except p. Since D_i is open, U would also be an $\mathfrak{X}$-neighborhood of p (cf. Theorem 6.3) and therefore p would also be an isolated point of $\mathfrak{X}$, which contradicts the definition of a discontinuum. Consequently, the D_i are discontinua. We have that $d(D_i) = \varepsilon_i > 0$. If we subdivide a set D_i in the same way as we have just subdivided $\mathfrak{X}$ into finitely many disjoint discontinua with a diameter $< \frac{\varepsilon_i}{2}$, then as a result we obtain at least two such sub-discontinua, and, by forming the union, we can form therefrom exactly two (non-empty) discontinua with a diameter $< \varepsilon_i$. This means that one can increase the number r of the sets in $\mathfrak{D}$ by 1 and by iteration of the process increase it by an arbitrary number. In particular, one can bring it to a power of 2, say 2^m. This completes the proof of the above assertion.

The remainder of the proof of the theorem proceeds completely analogously to the preceding proof. The only difference is that the covering sets D_i are now chosen disjoint so that they are even uniquely determined by the sequence $D_{i_1} \supset D_{i_1 i_2} \supset \ldots$ determined by the point $p_0 \in \mathfrak{X}$. Hence the mapping $p = f(x)$ turns out to be one-to-one. The continuity of the inverse mapping f^{-1} need not be proved separately because of the compactness of $\mathscr{C}$. This completes the proof of the theorem.

§ 34. Paving Theorem

We shall show in this section that a closed n-simplex $[\sigma] = [\sigma^n]$ really has the dimension n in the sense of the dimension concept which we introduced. For this purpose, the conditions (a_n) and (b_n) of the Definition 32.3 of dimension or (a_n') and (b_n') of Theorem 32.7, respectively, must be proved for the space $\mathfrak{X} = [\sigma]$. For (a_n) and (a_n') respectively this is relatively easy. On the other hand, the assertion (b_n) or (b_n'), respectively, of the paving theorem proper for the simplex $[\sigma]$ is not so easy to prove and requires some preparation, which is comprised in the so-called Sperner Lemma (cf. Theorem 34.1).

It has already been established by Theorem 30.6 that $\mathfrak{X} = [\sigma]$

possesses the property (a_n'): The open stars of the triangulation T of $[\sigma]$ consisting of all the faces of σ and likewise the stars of every normal subdivision $\mathsf{T}^{(\nu)}$ of T form an open covering of $[\sigma]$ of the order $n + 1$. Since the simplex diameter of the successive normal subdivisions become very small according to Theorem 31.6, (a_n') and thus that $\dim [\sigma] = n$ is proved. It is also easy to give closed ε-coverings of order $n + 1$ of $[\sigma]$. In the case $n = 2$, we obtain such a one in the form of the paving figure preceding Definition 32.3. There are no fundamental difficulties to generalize this paving to $n = 3$ and by induction to all n.

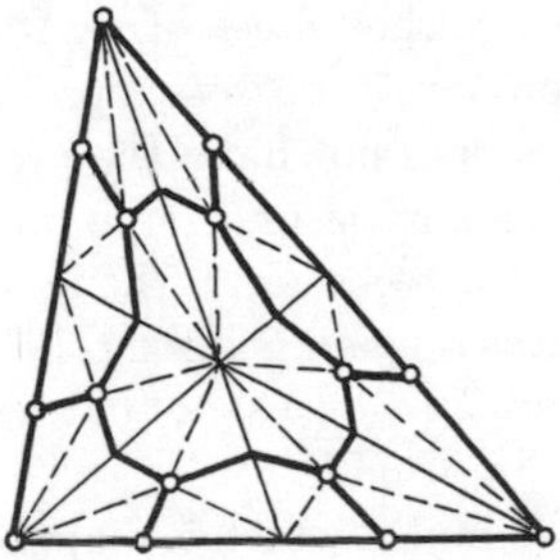

Fig. 9

One obtains other closed ε-coverings of the order $n + 1$ as follows: We subdivide an arbitrary one of the triangulations $\mathsf{T}^{(\nu)}$ just considered still further to $\mathsf{T}^{(\nu)\prime}$ and form the closures of those stars of $\mathsf{T}^{(\nu)\prime}$ which are assigned to the vertices of $\mathsf{T}^{(\nu)}$ as is indicated in Fig. 9. It is easily seen that in analogy to Theorem 30.6, such stars have points in common if, and only if, they belong to the vertices of the same simplex of $\mathsf{T}^{(\nu)}$, from which we recognize that the order of this covering is really $n + 1$.

34.1 The Sperner Lemma: *Let* $\sigma = \sigma^n = \mathfrak{p}_0 \ldots \mathfrak{p}_n$ *be an n-simplex,* $\mathsf{T} = \mathsf{T}^n$ *the corresponding triangulation of* $[\sigma]$, T' *an arbitrary subdivision of* T. *If to each vertex* $\mathfrak{p}'$ *of* T' *there is assigned a vertex* $\varphi(\mathfrak{p}') = \mathfrak{p}_i$ $(i = 0$ *or* $1 \ldots$ *or* $n)$ *of its carrier simplex in* T, *then there* *exists at least one n-dimensional simplex* σ_0' *in* T' *whose vertices can be mapped by* φ *into the set of all vertices* $\mathfrak{p}_0, \ldots, \mathfrak{p}_n$.

Proof: Let the number of n-simplexes σ_0' of T' of the sort indicated in the theorem be a. We shall prove, over and above the assertion of the theorem, by means of induction on n, that a is odd. For $n = 0$, the assertion of the theorem is trivial. Suppose it has already been proved for the dimensions $0, 1, \ldots, n-1$. Suppose the totality of all n-simplexes of T' are σ_i' ($i = 1, \ldots, s$). A face simplex $\tau' = \tau'^{n-1}$ of a σ_i' will be called a *distinguished* face of σ_i' if the vertices of τ' are mapped by φ into the set of all the vertices $\mathfrak{p}_1, \ldots, \mathfrak{p}_n$. Let a_i be the number of distinguished faces of σ_i'. If σ_i' has the property of the theorem, then σ_i' obviously possesses precisely one distinguished face—it is $a_i = 1$. If σ_i' does not have the property of the theorem, then either all the $\mathfrak{p}_1, \ldots, \mathfrak{p}_n$ occur among the images of the vertices of σ_i', moreover each one twice, and then obviously $a_i = 2$, or at least one of these vertices is lacking among the images, and then $a_i = 0$. Summarizing, we have in all cases that $a \equiv (\sum a_i) \bmod 2$, and it suffices to prove that $\sum a_i$ is odd.

Let τ' be an $(n-1)$-simplex which is mapped by φ into $(\mathfrak{p}_1, \ldots, \mathfrak{p}_n)$. Either τ' is an interior simplex of σ, and then it is a distinguished simplex consisting of precisely two of the σ_i'; therefore, it is counted twice in $\sum a_i$. Or, τ' lies on one $(n-1)$-dimensional face of σ; this must be the face $(\mathfrak{p}_1 \cdots \mathfrak{p}_n)$ inasmuch as others cannot map into $(\mathfrak{p}_1 \cdots \mathfrak{p}_n)$ under φ because of the carrier condition of the theorem. Then τ' is a distinguished face of precisely one of the σ_i' and hence is counted exactly once in $\sum a_i$. The number of simplexes of the second indicated sort is odd according to the induction assumption; the number of the first-named sort is odd, as we have just established, and thus $\sum a_i$ is odd. This completes the proof of the theorem.

34.2 Paving Theorem: *For each n-simplex* $\sigma = \sigma^n$, *there exists an* $\varepsilon > 0$ *such that every finite open* ε*-covering of* $[\sigma]$ *has order* $= n + 1$.

Proof: Let T be a triangulation of $[\sigma]$ consisting of all the face simplexes of σ including σ itself. The $n + 1$ stars of T form an open covering of $[\sigma]$. Let ε be a Lebesgue number of this covering. We assert that *every finite open ε-covering of $[\sigma]$ has at least the order $n + 1$.* To prove this, we consider an open ε-covering $\mathfrak{D} = \{D_i \mid i = 1, \ldots, m\}$ of $[\sigma]$. Let λ be a Lebesgue number of $\mathfrak{D}$ and suppose T' is so fine a normal subdivision of T that the diameters of the simplexes of T' are all $< \frac{\lambda}{2}$, and that the diameters of the stars of T' are therefore all $< \lambda$.

Let $\mathfrak{p}'$ be an arbitrary vertex of T'. On account of the choice of λ, the star of $\mathfrak{p}'$ is contained entirely in at least one of the sets D_i; we choose one of these sets D_i, call it D and set $D = \psi(\mathfrak{p}')$. Thus, each vertex $\mathfrak{p}'$ of T' is assigned to a well-defined set D_i. Because of the choice of ε, each set D_i is contained entirely in one of the $n + 1$ stars of T. We choose one of these stars, denote its midpoint by $\mathfrak{p}$, and set $\mathfrak{p} = \chi(D_i)$. Thus, each set D_i is assigned a well-defined vertex of σ.

Now if we let the vertex $\mathfrak{p} = \varphi(\mathfrak{p}') = \chi\psi(\mathfrak{p}')$ correspond to each vertex $\mathfrak{p}'$ of T', then this is obviously a correspondence as is considered in the Sperner Lemma. Therefore, there exists an n-dimensional simplex $\sigma' = \mathfrak{p}_0' \ldots \mathfrak{p}_n'$ of T' whose $n + 1$ vertices are mapped by φ into all the $n + 1$ vertices of σ. Hence, the sets $\psi(\mathfrak{p}_j')$, $j = 0, \ldots, n$, are $n + 1$ distinct sets D_i, and, for these indices j, we have that

$$\varnothing \neq (\sigma') \subset \bigcap_{j=0}^{n} st\, \mathfrak{p}_j' \subset \bigcap_{j=0}^{n} \psi(\mathfrak{p}_j').$$

Hence, $\mathfrak{D}$ has at least the order $n + 1$, which is what we had to prove.

This proves completely the assertion (b_n') and thus the equation $\dim \sigma = n$. The Brouwer Theorem 32.1 is proved at the same time. Also the dimension of an n-dimensional parallelepiped is thereby recognized to be n; one can certainly inscribe a suitable σ'^n in the parallelepiped and then apply Theorem 32.4. The corresponding fact holds for the dimension of a polyhedron with a triangulation of algebraic dimension n. We summarize all this in the next theorem.

34.3 Theorem: *A simplex, a parallelepiped, and a polyhedron with a triangulation of algebraic dimension n have the (paving) dimension n.*

§ 35. Embedding Theorem

From the comprehensive area of dimension theory, we can prove only one more, in any case, especially important and interesting, theorem—namely, the *embedding theorem* which was first proved by K. Menger and G. Nöbeling: *A compactum of dimension* $n \geqq 0$ *is homeomorphic to a subspace of the Euclidean space* R^{2n+1}. We have already seen earlier that a polyhedron of dimension n can always be geometrically realized in Euclidean space R^{2n+1} (see Assertion II in § 30). The embedding theorem generalizes this assertion to arbitrary compacta and shows the significance of the dimension concept insofar as the measure giving embedding dimension $2n + 1$ for polyhedra also suffices for the embedding of compacta of dimension n. Also if one ignores the exact dimension in the embedding theorem, one still obtains a significant result: The compact subsets of Euclidean spaces can be recognized as the compacta of finite dimension. The proof, which we subsequently will carry out in conjunction with the Alexandroff concept formation, makes use of a whole series of our previous principal results and distinguishes itself by the originality of its line of reasoning and special geometric intuitiveness.

We first introduce the concept of a nerve of a finite covering. Let $\mathfrak{D} = \{D_i \mid i = 1, \ldots, m\}$ be a finite covering of a space $\mathfrak{X}$. We assign to each set D_i the unit point $\mathfrak{e}_i$ of the Euclidean space R^m. If a subsystem of the D_i has a non-empty intersection $D_{i_0} \cap \ldots \cap D_{i_r} \neq \varnothing$, then we span the simplex $(\mathfrak{e}_{i_0} \ldots \mathfrak{e}_{i_r})$ by the corresponding vertices $\mathfrak{e}_i$. In this way, we obtain a subcomplex $\mathbf{N}$ of the unit simplex of R^m because the two conditions [S 1] and [S 2] of Definition 30.1 are satisfied; [S 1] is immediate according to the definition of $\mathbf{N}$ and [S 2] holds for every set of simplexes of the unit simplex. $\mathbf{N}$ and likewise every other realization of $\mathbf{N}$ is called a *nerve* of $\mathfrak{D}$. Obviously *the order of the covering* $\mathfrak{D}$ *diminished by* 1 *is equal to the dimension n of its nerve* $\mathbf{N}$. According to Proposition II of § 30, $\mathbf{N}$ can be realized in Euclidean space R^{2n+1}.

We now specialize and let $\mathfrak{D}$ be a finite open ε-covering of the compactum $\mathfrak{X}$ and let $\mathbf{N}$ be a realization of the nerve of $\mathfrak{D}$ in a Euclidean space. Let the vertices of $\mathbf{N}$ be $\mathfrak{p}_i$ $(i = 1, \ldots, m)$. We will give a continuous ε-mapping α: $\mathfrak{X} \to |\mathbf{N}|$—the so-called *Alexandroff mapping* of $\mathfrak{X}$ into $|\mathbf{N}|$. To this end, let x be a point of $\mathfrak{X}$. For $i = 1, \ldots, m$, we define a real-valued function φ_i as follows:

$$\varphi_i(x) = d(x, \complement D_i).$$

Since the D_i are open, the $\complement D_i$ are closed and $\varphi_i(x) > 0$ if, and only if, $x \in D_i$ (see Theorem 20.4). For no x are all the $\varphi_i(x)$ zero, so that one can form

$$\lambda_i = \lambda_i(x) = \frac{\varphi_i(x)}{\sum \varphi_j(x)} \text{ summed over } j = 1, \ldots, m.$$

Then we have $\sum \lambda_i = 1$. We set $\alpha(x) = \mathfrak{p} = \sum \lambda_i \mathfrak{p}_i$. If x lies in the sets $D_{i_0}, \ldots, D_{i_r}$, but in no other set D_i, then the $\lambda_{i_0}, \ldots, \lambda_{i_r}$ are $\neq 0$ but all the other λ_i are $= 0$, and $\mathfrak{p}$ lies in the simplex $(\mathfrak{p}_{i_0} \ldots \mathfrak{p}_{i_r})$ belonging to $\mathbf{N}$. Therefore, $\mathfrak{p} = \alpha(x)$ lies in $|\mathbf{N}|$.

That the Alexandroff mapping $\alpha(x)$ is an ε-mapping results from the fact that $\alpha^{-1}(\mathfrak{p})$ is always entirely contained in a set D_i inasmuch as it follows from $\lambda_i \neq 0$ that $x \in D_i$ and that $d(D_i) < \varepsilon$. The continuity of $\alpha(x)$ follows from the continuity of the functions $d(x, \complement D_i)$ (cf. Theorem 20.5). We formulate the above result as follows.

35.1 Theorem: *If* $\mathfrak{D} = \{D_i \mid i = 1, \ldots, m\}$ *is an open* ε*-covering of the compactum* $\mathfrak{X}$, *then the Alexandroff mapping* $\alpha(x) = \mathfrak{p}$ *yields a continuous* ε*-mapping of* $\mathfrak{X}$ *into the field* $|\mathbf{N}|$ *of nerves* $\mathbf{N}$ *of* $\mathfrak{D}$.

Now let $\mathfrak{X}$ be a compactum of dimension n, dim $\mathfrak{X} = n$. Then for every $\varepsilon > 0$ there exists a finite open ε-mapping $\mathfrak{D}$ of order $n + 1$. Suppose the nerve $\mathbf{N}$ of $\mathfrak{D}$ is realized in a fixed Euclidean space R^{2n+1}. The Alexandroff mapping therefore yields a continuous ε-mapping of $\mathfrak{X}$ into this R^{2n+1}. Now the space $\mathfrak{F}(\mathfrak{X}, R^{2n+1})$ of all continuous mappings of $\mathfrak{X}$ into R^{2n+1} is complete according to Theorem 25.2. The space $\mathfrak{F}_\varepsilon(\mathfrak{X}, R^{2n+1})$ of all ε-mappings of $\mathfrak{X}$ into R^{2n+1} is, according to Theorem 25.5, an open subspace of $\mathfrak{F}_\varepsilon(\mathfrak{X}, R^{2n+1})$. The intersection of all the $\mathfrak{F}_\varepsilon(\mathfrak{X}, R^{2n+1})$ or even the intersection of all $\mathfrak{F}_{\frac{1}{k}}(\mathfrak{X}, R^{2n+1})$, $k = 1, 2, \ldots$, is the space of all homeomorphic mappings of $\mathfrak{X}$ into R^{2n+1}, as was already noted in conjunction with Definition 25.3. If we can prove this intersection to be non-empty, our goal will have been reached. The Baire density theorem (see Theorem 21.7) serves us to this end. From its assumptions, the following is satisfied: $\mathfrak{F}(\mathfrak{X}, R^{2n+1})$ is complete and the $\mathfrak{F}_{\frac{1}{k}}(\mathfrak{X}, R^{2n+1})$ are open. If we furthermore show that all the $\mathfrak{F}_{\frac{1}{k}}(\mathfrak{X}, R^{2n+1})$ are dense in $\mathfrak{F}(\mathfrak{X}, R^{2n+1})$, we can deduce that the intersection of all the $\mathfrak{F}_{\frac{1}{k}}(\mathfrak{X}, R^{2n+1})$ is non-empty, and thus the embedding theorem would be proved. We shall accordingly next prove that $\mathfrak{F}_\varepsilon(\mathfrak{X}, R^{2n+1})$ is dense in $\mathfrak{F}(\mathfrak{X}, R^{2n+1})$.

Besides $\varepsilon > 0$, let a function $g \in \mathfrak{F}(\mathfrak{X}, R^{2n+1})$ and an arbitrary $\eta > 0$ be given. We shall construct an Alexandroff ε-mapping $\alpha \in \mathfrak{F}_\varepsilon(\mathfrak{X}, R^{2n+1})$ with $d(\alpha, g) < \eta$; then everything will be proved. We first use the uniform continuity of g; there exists a $\delta > 0$ such that $d(x, y) < \delta$ implies that $d(g(x), g(y)) < \frac{\eta}{6}$. Moreover, δ can also be taken $< \varepsilon$.

Let $\mathfrak{D} = \{D_i \mid i = 1, \ldots, m\}$ be an open δ-covering of $\mathfrak{X}$ of order $n + 1$. $\mathfrak{D}$ is also an ε-covering. It follows from $d(D_i) < \delta$ that $d(g(D_i)) \leqq \frac{\eta}{6}$. We choose a point $\mathfrak{q}_i$ in each set $g(D_i)$ and in the spherical neighborhood of radius $\frac{\eta}{6}$ about $\mathfrak{q}_i$ we choose a point $\mathfrak{p}_i$ such that the system of m points $\mathfrak{p}_i$ is in general position, which is possible according to Proposition B of § 30. We take these $\mathfrak{p}_i$ as the vertices of a realization of the nerve $\mathbf{N}$ of $\mathfrak{D}$ and construct α for this. We first estimate the diameters of the simplexes of $\mathbf{N}$ by estimating the lengths of the edges $\mathfrak{p}_i\, \mathfrak{p}_j$ of $\mathbf{N}$ (Theorem 29.2). If $\mathfrak{p}_i\mathfrak{p}_j$ is an edge of $\mathbf{N}$, then D_i and D_j have at least one point y in common and hence also $g(D_i)$ and $g(D_j)$ have the point $\mathfrak{y} = g(y)$ in common. Then

$$d(\mathfrak{p}_i, \mathfrak{p}_j) \leqq d(\mathfrak{p}_i, \mathfrak{q}_i) + d(\mathfrak{q}_i, \mathfrak{y}) + d(\mathfrak{y}, \mathfrak{q}_j) + d(\mathfrak{q}_j, \mathfrak{p}_j) < 4\,\frac{\eta}{6} = \frac{2}{3}\,\eta$$

holds. The diameter of a simplex in $\mathbf{N}$ is therefore at most equal to $\frac{2}{3}\eta$.

Now we estimate the distance $d(\alpha(x), g(x))$ between the two images of a point $x \in \mathfrak{X}$ under α and g. Let $x \in D_i$, $g(x) \in g(D_i)$; then $\alpha(x)$ is in every case contained in a simplex of **N** with the vertices $\mathfrak{p}_i$, and therefore $d(\alpha(x), \mathfrak{p}_i) < \frac{2}{3}\eta$. Combining, we have that

$$d(\alpha(x), g(x)) \leqq d(\alpha(x), \mathfrak{p}_i) + d(\mathfrak{p}_i, \mathfrak{q}_i) + d(\mathfrak{q}_i, g(x))$$

$$< \frac{2}{3}\eta + 2\frac{\eta}{6} = \eta.$$

From this we can conclude that $d(\alpha, g) < \eta$ since $d(\alpha, g) = \eta$ does not have to be considered according to Theorem 18.3. The result is the following.

35.2 Embedding Theorem: *A compactum $\mathfrak{X}$ of dimension n can be homeomorphically embedded in the Euclidean space R^{2n+1}.*

BASIC FORMULAS FROM SET THEORY

Let $\mathfrak{X}$ be a fixed basic set, and let $A, B, \ldots$ be subsets of $\mathfrak{X}$. Let $\mathfrak{Y}$ be another fixed set, and let $\mathfrak{A}, \mathfrak{B}, \ldots$ be subsets of $\mathfrak{Y}$. Union and intersection:

Associative laws:

(1) $A \cup (B \cup C) = (A \cup B) \cup C = A \cup B \cup C,$

(1′) $A \cap (B \cap C) = (A \cap B) \cap C = A \cap B \cap C.$

An arbitrary number of sets can also be combined associatively.

Distributive laws:

(2) $A \cup (B \cap C) = (A \cup B) \cap (A \cup C),$

(2′) $A \cap (B \cup C) = (A \cap B) \cup (A \cap C).$

(2) and (2′) respectively are valid for an arbitrary number of factors instead of $B \cap C$ and $B \cup C$ respectively.

The *complementary set* $\complement D = \mathfrak{X} - D$:

(3) $\complement(A \cup B) = \complement A \cap \complement B,$

(3′) $\complement(A \cap B) = \complement A \cup \complement B.$

(3) and (3′) respectively are valid for arbitrarily many factors in the parentheses.

Trace $\mathfrak{X}_T = \mathfrak{X} \cap T$ of $\mathfrak{X}$ with a subset T of $\mathfrak{X}$.

(4) $(A \cup B)_T = A_T \cup B_T$; (4′) $(A \cap B)_T = A_T \cap B_T$.

(4) and (4′) respectively are valid for arbitrarily many factors in the parentheses.

(5) $\complement_T A_T = (T - A_T) = (\complement A)_T$.

Mappings f of $\mathfrak{X}$ into $\mathfrak{Y}$:

(6) $f(A \cup B) = f(A) \cup f(B)$,

(6′) $f(A \cap B) \subset f(A) \cap f(B)$.

(7) $f^{-1}(\mathfrak{A} \cup \mathfrak{B}) = f^{-1}(\mathfrak{A}) \cup f^{-1}(\mathfrak{B})$,

(7′) $f^{-1}(\mathfrak{A} \cap \mathfrak{B}) = f^{-1}(\mathfrak{A}) \cap f^{-1}(\mathfrak{B})$.

(6)–(7′) are valid for arbitrarily many factors in place of $A \cup B$, $A \cap B$, $\mathfrak{A} \cup \mathfrak{B}$, $\mathfrak{A} \cap \mathfrak{B}$, respectively.

(8) If $\mathfrak{Y} = \bigcup_i \mathfrak{A}_i$ $(i = 1, \ldots, n)$ is a partition of $\mathfrak{Y}$, then $\mathfrak{X} = \bigcup_i f^{-1}(\mathfrak{A}_i)$ is a partition of $\mathfrak{X}$.

(9) $f^{-1}(\complement\mathfrak{A}) = \complement f^{-1}(\mathfrak{A})$.

(10) $f^{-1}(f(A)) \supset A$; (10′) $f(f^{-1}(\mathfrak{A})) \subset \mathfrak{A}$.

BIBLIOGRAPHY

Only the most important books are listed here which will enable the reader to go more deeply into the material treated in this little volume or to supplement it.

ALEXANDROFF, P. S.

[1] *Combinatorial topology*, Moscow-Leningrad, 1947 (Russian).

[2] *Combinatorial topology*, Graylock, Rochester, 1956 (English edition of [1]).

[3] *Introduction to set theory and the theory of functions*, Moscow, 1948 (Russian).

[4] *Einführung in die Mengenlehre und die Theorie der reellen Funktionen*, Berlin, 1956 (German edition of [3]).

ALEXANDROFF, P. S. and H. HOPF

[1] *Topologie*, Springer, Berlin, 1935.

BAUM, J. D.

[1] *Elements of point set topology*, Prentice-Hall, Englewood Cliffs, 1964.

BERGE, C.

[1] *Espaces topologiques*, Dunod, Paris, 1959.

BOLTYANSKY, V. G.

[1] *Homotopy theory of continuous mappings and of vector fields*, Trudy Mat. Inst. Steklova, No. 47 (1955) (Russian). Also see AMS Translations, Ser. 2, Vol. 7.

BOURBAKI, N.

[1] *Eléments de mathématiques*, Livre III: *Topologie générale*, Paris, Hermann, 1951.

BOURGIN, D. G.

[1] *Modern algebraic topology*, Macmillan, New York, 1963.

Bushaw, D.
[1] *Elements of general topology*, Wiley, New York-London, 1963.

Cairns, S. S.
[1] *Introductory topology*, Ronald, New York, 1961.

Čech, E.
[1] *Topologické prostory*, Nakladatelství Československé Akademie Věd, Prague, 1959.

Hall, D. W. and G. L. Spencer
[1] *Elementary topology*, Wiley, New York-London, 1955.

Halmos, P.
[1] *Naive set theory*, Princeton Univ. Press, Princeton, 1960.

Hausdorff, F.
[1] *Grundzüge der Mengenlehre*, Leipzig, 1914.
[2] *Mengenlehre*, 3rd edition, Berlin, 1935.
[3] *Set theory*, Chelsea, New York, 1957 (English edition of [2]).

Hocking, J. G. and G. S. Young
[1] *Topology*, Addison-Wesley, Reading-London, 1961.

Hurewicz, W. and H. Wallman
[1] *Dimension theory*, Princeton Univ. Press, Princeton, 1941.

Kamke, E.
[1] *Mengenlehre*, Sammlung Göschen 999/999a, de Gruyter, Berlin, 1955.
[2] *Theory of sets*, Dover, New York, 1950 (English edition of [1]).

Kelley, J. L.
[1] *General topology*, Van Nostrand, Toronto-New York-London, 1955.

Kelley, J. L., I. Namioka and co-authors
[1] *Linear topological spaces*, Van Nostrand, Princeton, 1963.

Köthe, G.
[1] *Topologische lineare Räume*, Springer, Berlin, 1960.

KOWALSKY, H. J.

[1] *Topologische Räume*, Birkhäuser, Basel-Stuttgart, 1961.
[2] *Topological Spaces*, Academic Press, New York, 1965 (English edition of [1] edited by William J. Pervin).

KURATOWSKI, K.

[1] *Topologie*, I, II. Warsaw, 1948, 1950.
[2] *Introduction to set theory and topology*, Addison-Wesley, Reading, 1960.

LEFSCHETZ, S.

[1] *Introduction to topology*, Princeton Univ. Press, Princeton, 1942.
[2] *Algebraic topology*, AMS, Providence, 1942.

MAMUZIĆ, Z. P.

[1] *Introduction to general topology*, Noordhoff, Groningen, 1963.

NÖBELING, G.

[1] *Grundlagen der analytischen Topologie*, Springer, Berlin-Göttingen-Heidelberg, 1954.

PATTERSON, E. M.

[1] *Topology*, Oliver and Boyd, Edinburgh-London, 1956.

PERVIN, W. J.

[1] *Foundations of general topology*, Academic Press, New York-London, 1964.

PONTRYAGIN, L. S.

[1] *Foundations of combinatorial topology*, Moscow, 1947 (Russian),
[2] *Foundations of combinatorial topology*, Rochester, Graylock. 1952 (English edition of [1]).

SEIFERT, H. and W. THRELFALL

[1] *Lehrbuch der Topologie*, Teubner, Leipzig, 1934, and Chelsea, New York, 1947.

SIERPIŃSKI, W.

[1] *General topology*, Toronto Univ. Press, Toronto, 1952.

SUPPES, P.

[1] *Axiomatic set theory*, Van Nostrand, Princeton, 1960.

Vaidyanathaswamy, R.

[1] *Set topology*, 2nd edition, Chelsea, New York, 1960.

Wallace, A. H.

[1] *An introduction to algebraic topology*, Pergamon Press, New York-London-Paris, 1957.

Whyburn, G.

[1] *Analytic topology*, AMS, New York, 1942.

Wilder, R. L.

[1] *Topology of manifolds*, AMS, New York, 1949.

INDEX

Including notes on some key terms